The history of cochlear implant technology is amazing and needs to be told. In the beginning, the idea of restoring hearing was considered too good to be true. Now, as a cochlear implant surgeon, I am a daily witness to the miracle of restored hearing. It is an indescribable joy to hear children born deaf develop normal language after surgery. Thank you Professor Clark for your endurance and marvellous achievements!

**Eva Karltorp**
Swedish medical specialist and
head of a cochlear implant team

Graeme Clark bravely went where no-one had gone before, breaking the barriers of sound perception for the deaf. He did this in a way that is inspirational, using multi-disciplinary teams to deal with a wide range of hearing research questions. His tenacity won him many battles: financial, scientific and personal. This book is a wonderful account of his work and how it has improved the quality of life for the hundreds of thousands of people now using the cochlear implant and for their families, friends and society.

**Jim Patrick**
Former Chief Scientist for Cochlear Limited

Criticised, opposed, ridiculed by peers and academia, Graeme Clark led a team to achieve what the world's greatest research institutes could not: the development of the bionic ear. *I Want to Fix Ears* relates how dedication to science, enduring faith, and a burning passion allowed him to achieve the impossible. "It was as though I was in constant dialogue with a supreme being," he says. A caring, passionate, and driven man, yet one of profound humility, Clark describes in his own words the highs and lows, the trials and the victories of his journey.

**Ernest Crocker**
Author, physician, NSW Chair, Christian
Medical and Dental Fellowship of Australia

Graeme Clark is one of the most important pioneers in biomedical engineering. In this book, he describes all aspects of his personal development from his family history, to practising medicine, and finally the founding of the Bionic Ear Institute. Following his initial inspiration, Clark describes the opposition from the scientific community, the Signing Deaf Community, and also from the public. The secret of his success was his ability to integrate clinical aspects, neurophysiology, biomedical engineering, ethical issues including the ethics of animal experimentation, and last but not least the very brave first patients. Clark demonstrates how a productive and ethical cooperation between academia, government, and industry can work. In addition, Clark demonstrates that faith in God can go hand in hand with scientific and academic pursuits in a fruitful symbiosis. Here are the facts that started the revolution in ear, nose, and throat surgery and in biomedical engineering.

**Roland Laszig**
Ear surgery pioneer in Germany

Graeme Clark's autobiography breathes the passion that has been his life: a desire to treat hearing loss declared in childhood and followed with dogged determination, culminating in one of the greatest medical inventions of the 20th century—the cochlear implant. Here one gains unique insights into the personal and professional challenges along the way, deeply rooted in family (traced back to the First Fleet) and grounded on Christian faith. Clark's story epitomises what is possible when the focus is upon the challenge rather than the self, and when this is embraced by the team and the community. The success is beautifully expressed by the testimony of those whose lives have been changed. A wonderful read—deeply inspiring.

**Stephen O'Leary**
Surgeon and Chair of Otolaryngology,
University of Melbourne

Our decision to choose a cochlear implant for our eldest daughter in 1991, after meningitis-induced deafness, was one of the most important decisions we ever made. The impact has been far beyond our dreams. Our daughter now has a university education, an interesting job, marriage, and a young son.

**Ann-Charlotte Gyllenram**
President of the Swedish Association of
Parents of Children with Cochlear Implants

I had the privilege of meeting Professor Clark years ago through his extraordinary publications, which led me to carry out my first cochlear implant in 1995. Since then, he has been the inspiration for hundreds of cochlear implants performed in Aragón. I know Graeme personally to be a kind and caring person, full of the same young and hopeful spirit that I first perceived in his brilliant career. Now, he stars in this exciting book, which offers a lesson in life and dedication.

**Hector Valles**
Director of Otorhinolaryngology,
University Hospital of Aragón, Spain

Graeme Clark's pioneering work in creating and developing the cochlear implant has transformed the lives of the profoundly deaf. Clark is a great Australian scientist, but also a world figure, a humanitarian driven by three factors: science, faith, passion. It is significant that Louis Pasteur's work—and faith—was an early inspiration. Clark's story is both powerful and touching, self-revelatory, but modest too. It deserves careful reading.

**Barry Jones**
Former Australian Minister for Science

The task Graeme Clark set himself—making the deaf hear—was truly biblical in proportion. Indeed, the Gospel of Mark (chapter 7) describes how Jesus made the deaf hear and the mute speak before an overwhelmed audience. Enthused as a boy by the writings of Louis Pasteur, Graeme developed his own *esprit préparé* or "prepared mind" by deep immersion in the hearing and speech sciences. Sustained by the Christian faith and a loving family, he overcame countless hurdles to make his dream of creating a wearable cochlear implant a reality, thus transforming the lives of countless deaf persons around the world.

**Gerard O'Donoghue**
Cochlear implant surgeon, Hunterian Professor
at the Royal College of Surgeons of England

I congratulate Graeme Clark on his outstanding achievement: the bionic ear. Graeme has a broad vision, is especially innovative and has great insight into human physical and mental conditions. He is creative, gentle and modest, and has transformed the lives of so many people. The origins and applications of the bionic ear are revealed clearly but modestly in this book. As well, the development of his professional career in Melbourne is especially fascinating as is the evolution of love between him and Margaret.

**Ian Macphee**
Former Australian Minister for Productivity

I have been very impressed by the emergence of the bionic ear as a practical proposition, but even more by the promise for the future that it seems to embody. It makes use of the arrangement in the cochlea for pitch recognition to bring electronic technology into direct functional relationship with the nervous system and the human consciousness. Maybe that unique relationship has no other parallel in the nervous system, and thus that direct link between electronics and physiology will find no other application to medicine. Nevertheless, I feel it may represent a new benchmark in the understanding of neural and mental function in terms of their physical components. Perhaps the work will not reach such a climax for centuries, but whatever may eventuate special credit will be made to Professor Clark and his colleagues for their pioneering and successful work.

**Sir Frank Macfarlane Burnet**
Nobel Laureate (Nobel Prize in Physiology or Medicine 1960)
First Patron of the Australian Bionic Ear Institute 1985

Inside the cochlear implant story

# I want to fix ears

Graeme Milbourne Clark

AC, FAA, FRS, (Hon) FRCS, Lasker Laureate

ISCAST Melbourne

© 2021 Graeme Clark
Published by ISCAST.
PO Box 40, Forest Hill, Victoria 3131, Australia
editor@iscast.org
www.iscast.org

ISCAST
CHRISTIANS IN SCIENCE AND TECHNOLOGY

ISCAST is the Institute for Christianity in an Age of Science
and Technology: a network of people, from students to
distinguished academics, exploring the interface of science,
technology, and Christian faith.

All Bible quotes are from the King James Version.

Photograph on page 9 by Empathy Photography.

Typeset in Warnock Pro.

ISBN: 978-0-6450671-0-1

National Library of Australia Cataloguing-in-Publication entry
Creator: Clark, Graeme Milbourne
Title: I want to fix ears: Inside the cochlear implant story /
Graeme Milbourne Clark
Subjects: Clark, Graeme Milbourne, 1935–
    Science–Australia
    Technology–Australia
    Biography–Australia

This book is dedicated to my wife Margaret, not only for invaluable assistance in its writing but also for her selfless support, wise counsel, help with English over 50 years and managing our large family.

I would also like to thank our children Sonya, Cecily, Roslyn, Merran and Jonathan; their spouses Ian, Matt, Peter and Marissa; and our grandchildren Elise, Monty, Tessa, Daniel, Noah, Rebecca, Oliver, Elijah, Nicholas, Stephanie, Alfred and Phoebe for enriching our lives.

I owe a debt of gratitude to my parents for their loving and wise counsel and to my siblings Robin and Bruce for their generous spirit.

# Abbreviations

ARC    Australian Research Council

BEI    Bionic Ear Institute

CID    Central Institute for the Deaf

DF    Deafness Foundation

ENT    Ear, nose, throat. ENT doctors are also known as otolaryngologists.

FDA    Food and Drug Administration, USA

GCF    Graeme Clark Foundation

GCI    Graeme Clark Institute for Biomedical Engineering, the University of Melbourne

HCRC    Human Communication Research Centre

JPC    John Pearce Centre

LCI    Lions Clubs International

LTU    La Trobe University

MLC    Methodist Ladies' College, Sydney

MU    Monash University

NAL    National Acoustics Laboratory

NHMRC    National Health and Medical Research Council of Australia

| | |
|---|---|
| NIH | National Institutes of Health, USA |
| NLA | National Library of Australia |
| RNTNEH | Royal National Throat, Nose and Ear Hospital |
| RPAH | Royal Prince Alfred Hospital |
| RVEEH | Royal Victorian Eye and Ear Hospital |
| SCM | Student Christian Movement |
| UMDOL | University of Melbourne Department of Otolaryngology |
| UMDOLEE | University of Melbourne Department of Otolaryngology and Electrical Engineering |
| UoM | University of Melbourne |
| UoS | University of Sydney |
| UoW | University of Wollongong |

# Acknowledgements

Writing a book is nearly an all-consuming effort. To bring it to fruition requires a number of dedicated people. Firstly, I would like to thank Debbie Mussett, who has worked tirelessly to format the drafts, prepare the photos at a high standard and organise appropriate meetings while undertaking a range of other responsibilities. I wish to thank the Revd Dr Chris Mulherin, Executive Director of ISCAST–Christians in Science and Technology, for facilitating the production of the book and for his helpful advice. That applies also to Michael Collie, Andrew Mulherin, Juliet Stanton, Anne Willett and Roslyn Jones. I am also greatly indebted to Paul and Margaret Drane from Pipeline Media, who have engaged with me professionally and personally over nearly 30 years to produce high-quality video productions.

I am grateful to the Department of Electrical Engineering at the University of Melbourne and Professor Mark Cook, Director of the Graeme Clark Institute for Biomedical Engineering, for providing support and facilities for the work to be completed. This has also been made possible through generous donations from the Cochlear Foundation, Mrs Pam De Sauty, the Graeme Clark Foundation and the Baranski Bequest.

The work was initiated at the University of Sydney and brought to fruition through the University of Melbourne in association with Cochlear Ltd. I am indebted to all the teams I have led in the Department of Otolaryngology at the University of Melbourne and the Royal Victorian Eye and Ear Hospital. Support from the deans and faculties of Medicine, Engineering and Science at the University of Melbourne has been crucial. The Bionic Ear Institute, University of Wollongong, St Vincent's Hospital in Melbourne, La Trobe University, National Information and Communications Technology of Australia and the Department of Engineering at the University of Melbourne have facilitated key stages in the research. This support also depended on research grants from the National Health and Medical Research Council of Australia, the Australian Research Council, the US National Institutes of Health and the Cooperative Research

Centres (CRC) program. The Deafness Foundation of Victoria, Lions Clubs International and the Channel 0/10 Telethon assisted greatly. I am also indebted to the bipartisan support at the federal and state level of politics. The Federal Government of Australia brokered its industrial development through a public interest grant and the State Government of Victoria established the first cochlear implant clinic in the world at the Royal Victorian Eye and Ear Hospital. The Adult Deaf Society and the auditory/oral deaf schools have provided essential support.

# Contents

# Foreword

*Science, faith* and *passion* best outline my personal story to develop the cochlear implant for severely/profoundly deaf people. *Science* was fundamental for understanding how we perceive electrical stimulation of the brain. *Faith* was needed to believe basic findings were applicable to the deaf person and that divine guidance was behind the enterprise. *Passion* was essential to sustain the effort. In addition, commitment was required of the team at the University of Melbourne and Cochlear Ltd to achieve a successful clinical outcome.

My working life has been directed to helping deaf people hear after my childhood experience of having a deaf father. When I asked him in his 90s what being deaf had been like, he said, "It's been an enormous handicap. It affects your whole life. There is nothing so embarrassing as not to be able to hear people properly; having to work and interview people and talk to them. So many people don't respond when you ask them to speak up."

My scientific journey was also inspired from a young age by reading the biographies *The Life of Pasteur* by René Vallery-Radot and *Madame Curie* by Eve Curie. I felt a great desire to make discoveries, too, and started with experiments in my mother's laundry and my father's pharmacy.

What started as an idealist's dream to achieve what many said was impossible has had a wonderful outcome, which I hardly dared to expect. Now to know that a multi-channel cochlear implant can allow severely/profoundly deaf people to hear whispered comments, communicate with others, engage in discussions at meetings and appreciate music, and to know that children can develop spoken language and achieve their true potential has been a great joy.

I have written much about our research on cochlear implants in scientific journals, showing how the work was based on a solid foundation. I believe it is now instructive to write more about my reactions to the events, give the inside story and explain with simple concepts the underlying science. I hope the book will help the next generation to be creative, and passionate

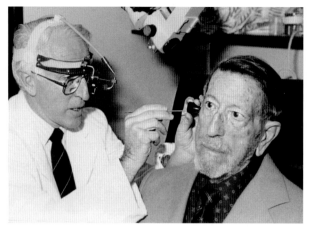

**Examining my father's ear in the University of Melbourne Royal Victorian Eye and Ear Hospital when he was in his 90s. "Being deaf has been an enormous handicap. It affects your whole life. There is nothing so embarrassing as not to be able to hear people properly."**

to make discoveries. As this process has been an audio-visual experience, this book itself is to be accompanied by a multimedia edition.

I have also been on a spiritual journey. From a young age I wanted to discover if there was meaning to our existence. This led unexpectedly to the experience of Christ Jesus in my life. I have tried to test the reality of this revelation along my journey and have found that science and faith in God are indeed compatible.

My initial research was done at the University of Sydney and then brought to fruition at the University of Melbourne and the Royal Victorian Eye and Ear Hospital, all with minimal funding. It was undertaken against intense criticism from scientists, clinicians and the Signing Deaf Community because most considered it would not succeed, was a waste of money, foolhardy, dangerous and unethical. In this book I explain how it was possible to overcome these challenges and establish the first public hospital-based cochlear implant clinic in the world at the Royal Victorian Eye and Ear Hospital in 1985. I also discuss how this development has given impetus to a new era of biomedical engineering allied to a discipline I have called medical bionics.

To facilitate a successful outcome, I also had to stimulate interest in industrial development of the bionic ear. That led to the creation of the Australian biomedical company Cochlear Ltd, which has been the world leader in implantable hearing technologies for the last 40 years. The collaboration of academia with industry is an example to follow.

The book highlights the function of normal hearing and the incidence and effects of severe/profound deafness. It then continues with the stories of six cochlear implant recipients, each involved at an important stage of the cochlear implant's development, telling how, as some describe it, the implant "has given them a new life." The book also provides a fresh personal account of how I managed the work that created the multi-channel cochlear implant. It also expands on the cochlear implant's development and longer-term benefits since the publication of my autobiography *Sounds from Silence*, published in 2000, and Mark Worthing's *Graeme Clark: The Man Who Invented the Bionic Ear* (2015). I have presented my thoughts and emotions in opening this new frontier in biomedical science, which required multidisciplinary research in a logical series of stages. The underlying science is outlined, and the ethical and religious issues are explored.

On this journey, there were crises to overcome as well as high points that encouraged all of us. Now it is exciting to see research being taken in new directions through the Graeme Clark Institute at the University of Melbourne with support from the Graeme Clark Foundation, a not-for-profit organisation.

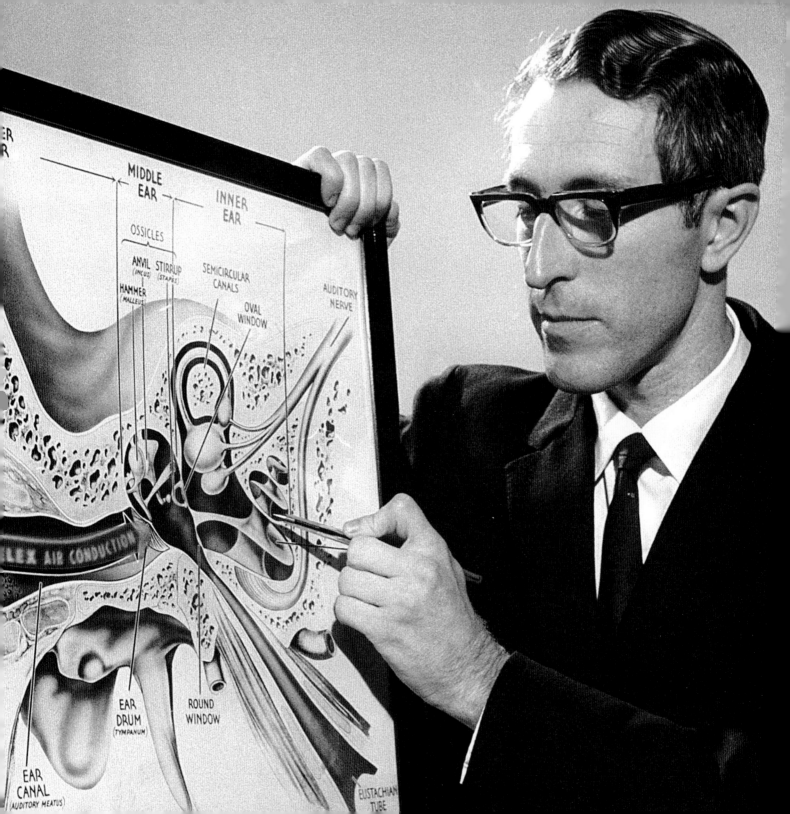

# Introduction

A multi-channel cochlear implant provides speech understanding for tens of thousands of severely or profoundly deaf people around the world. These people make up more than 0.1% of the overall population, and they receive little help from a hearing aid. In Australia approximately 20,000 people are profoundly deaf and 50,000 severely deaf. In the USA 340,000 are profoundly deaf and 750,000 are severely deaf.

As Helen Keller, who was blind and deaf, famously said, "Blindness cuts you off from things, but deafness from people." Deafness is classified as either mild, moderate, severe or profound. With the milder and moderate forms, deafness can be alleviated by amplifying the sound level with a hearing aid. However, when it is severe or profound, due to malfunction of the inner ear, the only effective solution is for the inner ear to be bypassed with a cochlear implant (also known as a bionic ear) and for the hearing nerve to be stimulated electrically to send signals to the brain.

When I commenced research in 1967, there was little that could be done to help severely/profoundly deaf people to hear. This is illustrated in a letter written in 1967 by ENT colleague Dr Les Caust to a patient who later received one of our cochlear implants. Les Caust said, "You will make the most of a pretty bad lot."

**Explaining my intention to insert multiple electrodes around the basal turn of the cochlea to stimulate the important speech frequencies on a place-coding basis in 1970.[1]**

Adults who develop spoken language before losing hearing can sometimes learn to lipread and still be able to communicate. Whatever their level of skill, however, they will require concentration to do so and become fatigued. Hearing in the presence of background noise will be particularly difficult. For some, it will result in loneliness, problems in coping with work and may even hasten the onset of dementia.

Children who are either born deaf or lose hearing before language is established (pre-linguistically deaf) will have all the difficulties experienced by the post-linguistically deaf person, but the plasticity of the brain at this stage may ameliorate the effects. However, normal spoken language is a skill that will require considerable training.

## Normal hearing

To best understand deafness, it is important to know the normal structure of the ear and its function before learning what happens when things go wrong and a cochlear implant is required. The structure of the ear, demonstrating its components, the outer (external), middle and inner ears, is shown in the diagram.

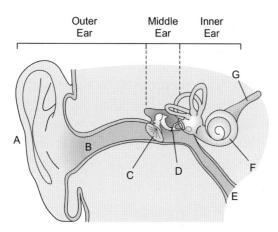

**A diagram of the outer, middle and inner ears and auditory nerve passing to the brain.**
A: pinna, B: external auditory canal, C: eardrum, D: ossicles, E: eustachian tube, F: cochlea and G: auditory nerve.[2]

The external ear collects sound vibrations which pass along the ear canal to cause the eardrum or tympanic membrane to vibrate. These vibrations are transferred to the ossicles in the middle ear: to the malleus (hammer) which is attached to the tympanic membrane, then to the incus (anvil) and finally the stapes bone (stirrup). The stapes footplate overlies the oval window opening into the inner ear. As the stapes footplate is 10 times smaller than the eardrum, the sound level is amplified according to that ratio. The vibrations in the fluid of the inner ear cause the basilar membrane to vibrate. This membrane lying across the inner ear canal vibrates selectively to different sound frequencies, and so it acts as a sound filter.

The vibrations of the basilar membrane are converted into electrical signals by inner and outer hair cells in the organ of Corti. The cells have hairs on their surface, and these hairs bend back and forth in the gelatinous tectorial membrane acting like a switch allowing electrical current to flow through the cells to the nerve fibres.

The cochlear or auditory nerves in the inner ear transmit patterns of neural electrical responses to five main nuclei in the brain where they are decoded to produce conscious experiences. But how consciousness occurs is still a mystery.

In the auditory system, information about both the time and the place of excitation are important for the coding of sound frequencies. With temporal coding, sound waves cause nerve electrical signals (action potentials) to occur in response to the varying energy of the sound waves. It is assumed that the brain decodes the signals by detecting the intervals between the action potentials of the neurons. At higher frequencies, the nerves don't fire every cycle, but a group or population of neurons does. With still higher frequencies, the firing becomes random. This temporal coding for frequency is "calculated" by the brain from the intervals between nerve action potentials.

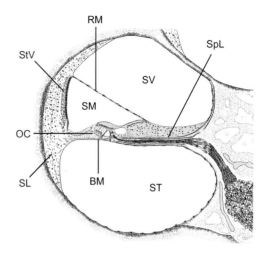

A cross section of the human cochlea showing the fluid-filled scala vestibuli (SV), separated from the scala media (SM) by the thin Reissner's membrane (RM). The scala media is separated from the scala tympani (ST) by the basilar membrane (BM), which is attached to the spiral lamina (SPL) internally and the spiral ligament (SL) externally. The hearing organ of Corti (OC) rests on this vibrating membrane.[3]

With place coding, the different regions of the cochlea that respond to different sound frequencies are each connected to nuclei in the brain, and so a frequency scale is preserved. This is referred to as tonotopic organisation and it may be likened to a piano keyboard with each key having a different frequency.

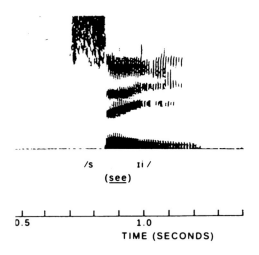

/s          ɪi /

(<u>see</u>)

0.5                    1.0

TIME (SECONDS)

**A spectrogram of the word "see."**

I considered speech understanding to be the greatest need of my severely/profoundly deaf patients so my main aim was to code speech frequencies, rather than only environmental sounds. I was challenged by some researchers with an interest in single-channel stimulation, who claimed that it was enough for these patients to have general awareness of sound and they informed me I was being overambitious. Speech is a complex auditory signal and so my challenge was to discover how to convert the auditory information received into meaningful electrical stimuli. This is discussed in later chapters of this book.

At any instant in time, the frequency spectrum of speech can be analysed. This is demonstrated for the word "see" in the diagram. The brain codes the consonant "s" as high frequency noise, and the vowel "i" as three resonant frequencies, known as formants. The voiced sound is the low frequency trace. Formant frequencies occur when the speech sounds resonate in a person's vocal cavities appropriate for each vowel, and these formants are essential for understanding speech. The spectrogram, such as that in the diagram, is helpful in understanding how speech can be analysed by cochlear implant speech processors.

# CHAPTER ONE

# Lives transformed by the bionic ear

My scientific studies aimed to advance human welfare. In setting out to restore hearing, I found many did not think this was possible. In fact, at the start of my research journey there were two major frontiers in medicine remaining: genetic engineering and the restoration of brain function. How would attempts to restore sensory and nerve deafness all turn out, and were they worth the risk? I have asked patients or parents who participated at critical times to speak for themselves.

## Rod Saunders
## The first University of Melbourne patient (1978)

Rod Saunders was most courageous in letting me carry out the first operation on him with Brian Pyman on 1 August 1978 as we were going into the unknown. By the end of the journey, Rod had become a good friend.

## Rod Saunders's story

Rod's eldest daughter, Christine Zygmunt, tells Rod's story.

As a result of a car accident in 1977, my father, Rod Saunders, lost his hearing. Except for a clumsy exchange of scribbled notes, he couldn't communicate with anyone. His passion for singing in his church choir was gone. I can remember sitting next to Dad in church, taking down and passing on hurried transcriptions of the minister's sermon. I could never keep up and Dad gave up. Gradually, his friends stopped visiting. Deafness can be an unseen affliction, but its impact can be both seen and felt. Dad became

**Rod Saunders conversing with his wife Margaret in 1979 soon after receiving the wearable speech processor.**

## Ears for the nerve-deaf

A TINY computer system being developed by a research team headed by Melbourne's Professor Graeme Clark could mean a new "hearing" world for sufferers of severe nerve deafness.

Professor Clark first encountered the problem of deafness as a boy when his father lost his hearing.

Now after 10 years' intense study into nerve deafness he is confident that he will be able to help people similarly affected — five percent of the deaf in Australia.

Work on the computer is being carried out mainly within the Department of Otolaryngology at Melbourne University. Professor Clark, also an ear, nose and throat surgeon, has headed the Department since its inception seven years ago.

"Nerve deafness is the last frontier in diseases of the ear," Professor Clark said. "Whereas middle-ear deafness — the other major cause of deafness and quite different from nerve deafness — has been largely overcome with surgery and hearing aids, there is still no significant help for a number of those who suffer severe or complicated nerve deafness."

However, help could be on the way with the computer system which will soon be implanted for the first time in a patient. Professor Clark naturally cannot predict when the computer might be available for wide-spread use. Even if the tests are successful, he says, it will take many months to evaluate the whole procedure.

Professor Clark said a computer, together with tiny electrodes, will be implanted in the inner ear of the patient. These will be linked with a tiny processor-transmitter, the size of a hearing aid, worn behind the ear. These would then take over the function of the ear.

Even if successful, the computer system will not enable perfect hearing. It will not pick up high fidelity sound and there will be some "background" noise. However, patients should be able to hear and understand normal speech.

— DEIDRE NOLAN

**Professor Graeme Clark.**

**The report in the *Women's Weekly* on 4 May 1977 by Deidre Nolan.**

very depressed and isolated. In despair, he tried to learn lipreading but failed miserably. The outlook was bleak.

Dad was cut off from everyday conversation and banter simply because it was too arduous to write everything down on paper. In the months following his accident, Dad was confined to his recliner chair in the lounge room where he spent much of his time reading. The dreaded pad of paper and pencil lay on the small table next to him, a constant reminder of the isolated world to which he now belonged.

For the most part, Dad's life after his accident was characterised by loneliness and depression, until there was a glimmer of hope. Mum just happened to pick up a copy of the Australian *Women's Weekly* in an outpatients' waiting room at St Vincent's Hospital which featured experiments for a "bionic ear." He made a few enquiries, which led to a meeting with Professor Clark. The rest is history.

Although Dad was desperate for a chance to hear again, for the rest of the family it was a rather scary journey into the unknown. Dad's view was that he had nothing to lose and that, perhaps, other deaf people would also benefit from such a device in the future. Professor Clark clearly explained the possible problems that might be faced with the operation so that Dad understood the risks.

**Rod Saunders using the wearable speech processor for the first time to buy a magazine.**

Nevertheless, there was a degree of secrecy surrounding Dad's operation, due to concerns that the outcome was uncertain. About a month following the procedure, Dad underwent the first "test" to see if the implanted device facilitated sound. After some technical hiccups, Dad recognised some sounds and I remember when the news broke in the media. On the way home from the press conference, Mum was amazed to hear herself being interviewed on the radio news bulletin. Now the family could openly share the excitement of this amazing medical achievement. Dad was very pleased with himself that he had recognised *God Save the Queen* and *Waltzing Matilda*. Of course, these were very early days and Dad could only "hear" as long as he was connected to an immoveable wall of computers. I so admire Dad's commitment to attending the University of Melbourne Department of Otolaryngology (UMDOL) several times a week where he was taught to interpret these strange new electronic sounds so that he could eventually understand speech. Sometimes he would come home, almost shell-shocked following a testing session, as the technicians tried to refine the device. He complained of being bombarded unrelentingly with all sorts of sounds, including "bangs and pops in his head," as he put it. On the other hand, I recall how happy he was to have learned a new song, *Up There Cazaly*, which he had never heard before. He could sing it in tune and was quite proud of himself. He was even asked to sing it on the Channel 0/10 Nerve Deafness Appeal in 1979.

About a year after Dad's operation, a portable speech processor was developed which allowed him to "hear" at home, instead of having to be attached to a bank of computers.

**With Rod's eldest daughter Christine Zygmunt holding a backup model of the multi-channel cochlear implant that Brian Pyman and I inserted into Rod on 1 August 1978 at the Royal Victorian Eye and Ear Hospital.**

However, it was a far cry from today's compact device. The unit had to be carried like a shoulder bag and required the use of a large microphone attached by a cable. Whenever we wanted to talk to Dad, we had to pass the microphone around as in a press interview. This tended to make conversation rather self-conscious and formal, something the later compact devices with inconspicuous microphones definitely remedied.

The early versions of the speech processor required many hours of testing to refine. During the early years, Dad used to say that he relied on lipreading in conjunction with the bionic ear to understand what we were saying. However, I remember having a conversation with him in the garden when, suddenly, his face seemed to go blank, followed by a look of panic as he rushed inside to replace the batteries in his processor. Only then could our discussion continue. On another occasion, Dad was sitting in the back seat of the car and my sister and I were discussing our father's quirks when suddenly he entered into the conversation to defend himself. It was apparent that he could hear quite well with his cochlear implant even with our backs to him. We had to be more discreet in future.

For fourteen years, prior to his death, Dad lived with me, my husband and four boys in Emerald, a semi-rural township in the Dandenong Ranges on the outskirts of Melbourne. When his boisterous grandsons were a little too raucous, Dad used to comment that he was fortunate to be able to switch off his "ear" to enjoy a little peace and quiet. All humour aside, I am proud of the commitment and fortitude Dad showed to the initial experiment and to refining successive prototypes of the cochlear implant.

Because Dad lived with me, I sometimes accompanied him to special functions such as when he met the Queen or the Prime Minister. Most of all, I valued getting to know the dedicated research team and Professor Clark himself. I have such admiration for this selfless man, not only for what he gave my father and his family, but for the hope he has given to countless others now and in the future.

Initially, some may have said that Dad's life ended with his accident, but in fact, as a result of the bionic ear, his life took on an entirely new direction. Graeme Clark didn't just restore Dad's hearing but rebuilt his self-esteem and filled his life with purpose.

## Graham Carrick
## The first Cochlear Ltd/University of Melbourne patient (1982)

After the Australian Government created Nucleus/Cochlear Ltd to develop the University of Melbourne's cochlear implant, I became responsible for its clinical testing on six patients. Graham Carrick was the first to have it implanted. I recall him saying how good it was to be able to play a more active role as a father. He was also pleased when he went for a license and his directional microphones allowed him to hear a test signal from further away than the examiner, who was left in a state of awe and disbelief. Graham went on to help us in many ways, including being on the telethons to raise money for further research.

## Graham Carrick's story

I was not born with a hearing impairment. I arrived kicking and screaming and was pronounced "normal." In fact, I proved to be just that. Until I was four years old, I was an active, outgoing and wilful child. I would have given little thought then to the problems and frustrations of the deaf. Indeed, why should I?

It was when I was four, however, that I suffered severe burns to much of my small frame. Six months of intensive care and many years of outpatient's treatment followed as

I gradually recovered. The possibility that the large doses of drugs may have side effects was discussed at the time of the accident, but it was not until more than a year later it was confirmed that I had a hearing loss which was diagnosed as drug-induced.

As there was a complete change in my nature, this prompted a more thorough assessment of my hearing. At the age of eight, I was transferred to a special school for the oral deaf, to learn to lipread and use any residual hearing I had with a hearing aid. I became sullen, stubborn and withdrawn. It became more and more difficult, yet more and more important, to achieve the equality I sought. As I grew older, I was made more aware of the things I could not do rather than the things I could do, which shattered my confidence.

Confidence, or indeed the lack of it, plays such a vital role in a person's wellbeing and as a teenager I felt alone in a hostile environment. At 21, those threads I had clung to snapped when suddenly, at work, what remained of my hearing vanished in a shock of sound within my head. My world became silent. With the silence of being profoundly deaf I became completely reliant on lipreading. My command of vocabulary and speech was good, since I had had sufficient years of normal and partial hearing in which to become competent. I did not feel part of the Deaf Community as I did not use sign language to communicate, yet neither did I feel comfortable in the company of hearing people. To most people I appeared "normal." Deafness is not a visible handicap and consequently attracts little in the way of help and support from the community at large. There is little understanding of the problems, particularly in the area of employment. I had difficulty unwinding and relaxing, and for much of the time I was living on my nerves. Life was a real struggle in the years prior to receiving my first cochlear implant. No one knows just how much is missing from the life of a deaf person.

It was almost by accident that at 34 I became involved in the bionic ear program at the Royal Victorian Eye and Ear Hospital (RVEEH). An ear infection led me to visit a specialist who felt I might be the type of patient to fit into the program. At this time the implant was still in the experimental stage, but I was profoundly deaf and thus had nothing to lose. I was able to remember the sound of speech and other everyday noises

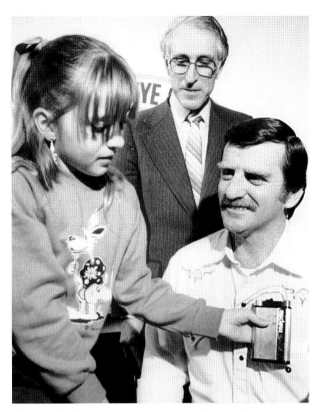

**With Graham Carrick: a symbol of hope for our telethon in 1982.**

which, at the time, was a prerequisite. I underwent and passed a series of intricate and exhausting tests and some two years later I underwent the eight-hour operation which involved implanting a coil into a cavity made by the surgeon in the bone behind my ear. There had been three similar operations about three years earlier with a prototype model. However, mine was the first operation with the new device. Australia was actually pioneering this type of medicine.

The day for "switch on" was difficult for everybody concerned, full of tension and worry lest it fail. But what a monumental day it was, the first time it was switched on, especially when it took a little while for the first sound to be heard. Initially, there was no response, until the right combination of tone, pitch and volume was entered via a computer and I heard a sound, like a gong. My first sound in 17 years! There were quite a number of teary eyes.

My journey was at a time when there was fear and apprehension, but also anticipation and a whole lot of hope. From that moment, an enormous amount of work went into making the sounds become language. Nothing sounded the same as it was, but for me it was as music to my ears. Looking back on it now, at every clinic visit the speech processor was tweaked and fine-tuned more. Things were also changing in the

Carrick house. Things as simple as the ladies calling out for a new roll of toilet paper or chastising the girls for fighting. I earned my front-end loader licence too, which had already been refused me due to my deafness.

I had to adapt to what was, for me, almost a brand-new language. The sounds I heard were mechanical, not like speech as we hear it, and I had to learn to interpret these sounds. At first, the noise was sometimes difficult to bear, but with the passage of time and with patience and practice the device has become invaluable. A number of other operations have been done since and the success rate has been encouraging. I can now understand some speech without lipreading. My lipreading skills have actually improved by 100%. My confidence in myself has been buoyed with a new-found ability and achievement in what had been considered out of reach. Music, though far from being relaxing, is discernible as music and this is truly considered a bonus since the speech processor was developed first and foremost for speech.

I don't have to rely on my family to answer the door and, as I hear the dogs, I know someone is coming. It does a lot for me at home. I have two small dogs and I can tell the difference when they bark. But I can chastise them for their rowdy barking and hear the birds in the trees, an aeroplane passing, the kettle boiling and the water running.

I used to use the phone to call people I knew. I would hear them at the other end, but I could only understand small words like "hello," "yes," "no," and the names of people I knew. This was handy in case I wanted someone to come to my house in case of an accident. The one achievement I am now proud of more than any other is my ability to converse over the telephone. It was another milestone. Initially, while in the clinic, I made a test call to my mum saying, "Is that you, Mum? This is your son Graham speaking." And I recall I asked her to say, "One, two, three," which I heard clearly. Since then, much work has gone into being able to use the phone. These days I can have almost normal conversations.

I am picking up a word here and there from the radio, but this did not happen in the early days. However, sometimes it can be confusing. I heard the sound from a cow at the beach. How could that be? But the noise sounded again, and I realised that the sound was not from a cow but from the horn of a big cargo ship. It pays to know where you are and use logic to work it out.

As far as my job is concerned, I am doing better there as people are now talking to me more often and I am more able to do things I couldn't do before. So, there are a lot more benefits than just listening to music.

I hope the cochlear implant will go on to change the lives of many, many people of all ages and from many walks of life. I have seen the latest cochlear unit. It is about half the size of the one I've got. One must be willing to put quite a lot of hard work into making it work for you, but the more you put into it, the more you will get out of it.

Most of us have nothing to lose in having the operation. I personally felt it would benefit my family as well as myself. So I gave it a go. In 1987, nearly three years since my operation, I found myself still learning to use it. It is easier now than it was then and there are always new developments happening to improve the speech processor.

I became the Victorian representative for the cochlear implant. I hope to continue to help as much as possible for people with implants.

## Professor Jennie Brand-Miller FAA
## The first academic to have the cochlear implant (1998)

Below, Professor Jennie Brand-Miller shares her story. Being an academic, I can identify with the demanding acoustic environment she faced. She received her first implant in 1998 from my colleague Professor Bill Gibson in Sydney, 20 years after we had carried out our first implant in Melbourne. At the time of her surgery, our research had been superbly engineered by Cochlear Ltd.

### Jennie Brand-Miller's story

Talking to me, you would never guess that I'm totally deaf in both ears. Thankfully, I am the recipient of two cochlear implants, the first one fitted when I was 46 years old and the second one at 55. This technology allows me to live a conventional life. I was born with apparently normal hearing and I went to a regular school, followed by university and a PhD. But over the next 20 years, I gradually lost my hearing while I worked my way up the academic ladder to Professor of Human Nutrition at the University of Sydney (UoS). Today, I am also the author of a popular series of diet books that has collectively sold 3.5 million copies worldwide in 12 languages. These achievements have only come about since my first cochlear implant.

I recall a night when, as a teenager, I had girlfriends to sleep over and one of them said, "Your mother is calling." I wondered why she could hear this, and I could not. I mentioned it to my parents, who in due course arranged for a hearing test. It turned out that I had moderately severe hearing loss. This was a big surprise, because there were no relatives with hearing loss. I needed a hearing aid which I managed to "lose," and the next one too. Hearing aids were not "cool."

In high school and as a student at university I remember saying, "Pardon?" and, "Can you say that again?" often. At the age of 25, I was offered my first real job as Lecturer in Nutrition. I was over the moon, but I knew I'd need a hearing aid if I were to hear students' questions. But the ENT specialist whom I consulted at the time told me that I should not have accepted the job. A little seed of doubt was planted that I was not good enough.

And slowly but surely, over the course of two decades, I lost most of the hearing in both ears and a lot of self-esteem. Indeed, my right ear lost all its residual hearing after a dental procedure and I wore a bi-cross hearing aid for 10 years. The decline was an emotionally painful process. I was embarrassed when I couldn't answer questions that were put to me. I dreaded being considered stupid in a world of intellectuals. I learned to avoid difficult hearing situations. Any gathering of people, round table meeting, and any noisy environment was stressful.

The telephone became a source of great torment. People's names escaped me, and transcribing numbers, addresses and dates was impossible. I became dependent on other people to transcribe my voicemail. I gradually lost the ability to enjoy television and movies. Public address announcements made travel difficult: I went to the wrong gate;

**"I encourage my students to follow Graeme Clark's example and question authority, challenge the prevailing wisdom and reject the status quo." Professor Jennie Brand-Miller**

I missed flights. At work, I was asking students to write questions on a piece of paper and to hand them to the front. Even in a quiet one-to-one conversation in my office, I was missing key words.

So, after 20 years in academia, I was ready to resign, and it felt like resigning from life. But a chance meeting resulted in a miracle and my life did a complete about-face. I'd been reading newspaper reports about cochlear implants with great interest. I knew that Professor Graeme Clark at the UoM had developed the world's first bionic ear and that Cochlear Ltd was one of the most successful biotechnology companies in the world. I'd also attended a seminar given by the newly-appointed Chair of Otolaryngology at the UoS, Professor Bill Gibson. I didn't hear most of what he said, although I had a feeling that we might meet again.

I decided to look up papers on cochlear implantation in the university library. I read that Bill Gibson was implanting children and even tiny babies. My brave hearing-impaired friend Judy decided she'd have one. I'd met Judy years before at assertiveness training for the hearing-impaired. Later that day, I was looking at old photos and noticed that she looked amazingly similar to one of the bridesmaids in a wedding photograph. It turned out it *was* her! Judy ignored those who said that you couldn't have a cochlear implant in one ear and a hearing aid in the other. She went ahead, and she inspired me to do likewise.

So, in 1998, I began the process of being considered for implantation. I knew I was pushing boundaries because I still had some useful hearing in the left ear. But the right ear was useless, and in my mind, I had nothing to lose. In Bill Gibson, I had the best surgeon in the world. In Monica Bray, I had the warmest, most thoughtful audiologist I could imagine. As I was being wheeled into theatre, I remember Bill saying something along the lines of "… must make sure I'm doing the right ear."

That deaf ear came back to life slowly but surely and my career took off like jump leads to a flat battery. Learning to hear again was exciting but it wasn't instant, and I had to be patient. The implanted ear had been deaf for a decade. Interestingly, I found the combination of hearing aid and cochlear implant synergistic. There were sounds I hadn't heard for decades and I often asked, "What's that noise?" It took at least a year, but the telephone was no longer an instrument of torture. I used the speaker option that gave me the best of both worlds. My whole outlook on life changed. I was actually bursting with pride, so proud of this cutting-edge Australian technology. I enjoyed having a conversation and then surprising the person by asking if they knew they were talking to someone who was totally deaf.

During the next few years, the residual hearing in the left ear declined to the extent that a hearing aid was no longer helpful. I started to wear just the multi-channel cochlear implant by itself. It was a bit tough. Noisy situations were hard, and I no longer listened to music. I knew people were having bilateral cochlear implantation, but Professor Gibson told me that I did not meet the criteria because my balance had been affected by the first operation. They wouldn't risk the second.

But then another ENT assessed my balance. I learned that I had defective responses in both ears which meant I had nothing to lose by having the second implant. This time, the ear responded almost immediately to stimulation. Within two weeks, I was lifting my mobile phone to my new ear.

With two bionic ears, life took another leap forward. The joy of listening to music returned. Noisy restaurants and meetings became manageable. I found the confidence to accept any invitation to speak and to travel the world alone to promote my research and my books. I volunteered for Cochlear Ltd's clinical trials. I made the most of the new hardware and new programs for hearing in noise and quiet.

My new Cochlear Ltd N7 speech processors are a quantum leap forward. They are linked by Bluetooth to my iPhone. The quality of sound is superb. I have fallen in love with Spotify and listening to all genres of music. I also love listening to podcasts on the way to and from work. If someone rings me while I'm listening, the podcast stops automatically, and I can answer the call with my multi-channel cochlear implant. I can interrupt the podcast by saying, "Hey, Siri! Ring so-and-so." I can make advanced changes to the map if I want to. For example, I can change the mix between external noise and internal noise when using the telephone or listening to a podcast.

There are many aspects of cochlear implants that are surprising. The clarity of hearing in a quiet environment is stunning—I rarely miss a word. I can detect accents and identify them with reasonable accuracy. The intelligibility of television is excellent, especially the news (but I do like the captions on Netflix). But most of all, I love the fact that the newest generation of software has a new map called Focus Forward which makes it relatively easy to have a conversation in a really noisy room. It works like a charm, so much so that my voice level is not high enough for the environment and people ask me to repeat what I say! The irony is that my hearing is improving while my friends are struggling with age-related hearing loss. Lately, I keep saying to myself that this is better than real ears!

I have Professor Graeme Clark to thank for all this. His story and my story have some things in common. We both faced scepticism, which is normal in science, and sometimes downright vocal opposition. In time, he won many prestigious awards, including a Clunies Ross Award in 1992 for contributions to Australian Science and Technology and many other awards. In 2003, I was the lucky recipient of a Clunies Ross Award. Ironically, his research and its application made my research and its application possible. But there, the comparisons end. Professor Clark's knowledge, skills, doggedness and faith resulted in the very first recreation of a human sense.

Graeme's experiences inspired me to be gracious under fire as well—even when the comments get ugly and personal. When I'm invited to give graduation addresses, I often tell Graeme's story, how he questioned authority, challenged the prevailing wisdom and rejected the status quo. And I encourage them to do likewise.

How do you thank someone who has given you back something unbelievably precious and uniquely human—the ability to listen and participate in a normal conversation with another human being?

## Sophie Li
## A young person to have implants and be an advocate (1993)

Sophie came to the RVEEH having had a Cochlear Ltd device implanted at age four in the USA. Her father, Li Cunxin AO, and mother, Mary, were both leading ballet dancers and had come to settle in Australia. Her father also became well-known through his book *Mao's Last Dancer*. Sophie's language and poise were outstanding, and I had memorable events in front of TV cameras demonstrating how fluent a profoundly deaf child could be with a cochlear implant.

## Sophie Li's story

It is an absolute honour to have been asked to write a small something for Professor Graeme Clark! Graeme is a most humbling person with an insatiable curiosity in the people who wear his invention, cochlear implants. Just writing this has already given me goosebumps. I was in Ireland travelling at the time, and I then jumped on a call with my mother back in Australia, whose immediate reaction was again how grateful she was for Clark's ingenuity in dreaming up the cochlear implant. The reason being, my life without the invention would have been very different. Not in a bad way; just different.

I have always liked Professor Clark. While Professor Clark was not involved in the beginning of my journey, we quickly became acquainted when my family moved from Houston in the USA to Melbourne, Australia, in 1995, when I was six years old. One of our first meets was when I was seven years of age. It was a function with their Imperial Highnesses Prince and Princess Akishimo of Japan in 1995. I had to give a small speech and present a gift alongside Professor Clark.

A photo for the local newspaper was taken. I was in my sports uniform with runners on and my hair in two pigtails. Professor Clark didn't seem to mind! As I got older,

"Today, we have a special close bond as mother and daughter. I can talk to my mother about anything." Sophie Li and her mother Mary.

I would go on to other significant events with Professor Clark—to meet with the former President of the Republic of China, President Jiang Zemin, on his official visit to the Bionic Ear Institute (BEI) on 7 September 1999 and also the former Australian Prime Minister, John Howard. However, I think my most memorable time with Professor Clark was when we were on television along with Rod Saunders and the TV host surprised me with the chance to tap away with *Tap Dogs*. What fun!

I didn't mind meeting these important people, but I had agreed to be part of these events because I had always liked Professor Clark as a person. He would greet me warmly with a twinkle in his eye and ask away about what I was doing in that time of my life. He genuinely wanted to get to know me and those conversations were what I always looked forward to.

Growing up with cochlear implants ... I won't lie; it was hard. It was difficult being different from other children, especially when I was already different to other deaf children around my age as they didn't have cochlear implants. It wasn't common during my childhood. People would get confused between hearing aids and cochlear implants, and my family members were often the experts in the matter, even though we didn't know half of it ourselves. We were just stumbling along blind, celebrating milestones and tackling problems as they came.

However, only my mother knew intimately how much work I still had to go through to get the best out of the cochlear implants. I received my first implant when I was four

**LEFT TO RIGHT: Pauline Trinh, Sian Neame, President Jiang Zemin, Professor Clark and Sophie Li on the official visit of the President of China to the Bionic Ear Institute on 7 September 1999.**

years old in Houston, USA. Many people are surprised when I say that I did not start speaking and hearing like other four-year-olds. I had to start again, recognising electrical signals and turning them into sounds, which would then become words, phrases and sentences. It required speech therapy every morning, noon and night. The intense training of my hearing and speech was relentless. My mother never took a moment of rest. I would also do it again in school before class started in the morning, while friends would be outside playing and laughing and during lunchtime. When I had friends over to play, my mother would even sometimes correct me in front of my friends when I pronounced a word wrong. My friends would be bewildered and fascinated at the same time. I just wanted the floor to swallow me up. I would ask my mother to stop embarrassing me and she would just say, "When you get it right, Sophie, then I'll stop!" Deep down, I knew that asking her was fruitless. She was a tornado: unstoppable.

However, I also knew deep down that my mother was doing the best for me. I also knew she loved me fiercely and without question. She would drop everything if she had to be at my side. I knew she was trying to do what was best for me. Today, we have a special close bond as mother and daughter. I can talk to my mother about anything.

Looking back makes me very thankful for what I have because now as a deaf adult, I have a choice that was never available before Professor Clark's invention: I can now choose to switch off my cochlear implants and be part of the deaf world or switch them back on and be instantly in the hearing world, anytime and anywhere in the world. I am forever in Professor Clark's and my mother's debt.

While the cochlear implant is not perfect or even ideal, it is enough for me and my mother.

## Sian Neame
## The youngest child, at two years, to have an implant (1990)

As head of the Cochlear Implant Clinic, head of the School of Audiology and as a senior surgeon, I had tracked Sian's case very carefully. Ultimately, I was responsible for the outcome and I had not faced the question of surgery on a child as young as Sian with some residual hearing. I felt some reassurance that Field Rickards and I had developed a means of diagnosing hearing loss at young ages by recording brainwaves and was confident of the severity of her hearing loss.[4] I did not want to risk losing any useful residual hearing.

Sian's mother Anne tells her story through her diary entries of events.

## Sian Neame's story

**Friday 5 May 1989.** This day was a defining moment in all of our lives. Sian was 18 months old and the youngest of our three children, having two older brothers Liam (six-and-a-half years old), and Lachlan (nearly four). I had booked her in for an audiologist appointment at Frankston Hospital. I don't remember being overly concerned about her hearing. Sian was very alert, and it never crossed my mind that she could not hear. She had passed the hearing test at the health centre, and so I naively assumed that her hearing was fine. My mother had expressed concern about her hearing, and I think that is what prompted me to get an appointment for her.

The initial diagnosis was that Sian was profoundly deaf in one ear and severely deaf in the other. A young audiologist gave this diagnosis at Frankston Hospital. From memory, I think this was the first time he had given such a bleak diagnosis to parents. One I believe that he never forgot. This set into place a whirlwind of appointments with a whole battery of specialists. At that point it felt like my life came crashing down.

I knew nothing about deafness, my only experience being a cousin's grandmother who was deaf and shouted to talk. I was scared of her as a child and couldn't understand her speech. The other was a girl with a hearing impairment in a ballet class when I was young. I thought she spoke in a strange way.

Later that day I went to see our GP. He was a bit sceptical about the diagnosis, suggesting that we should not be too disillusioned yet. The diagnosis may not be as bad as it seemed. He organised an appointment to see a local ENT surgeon the following Monday. Unfortunately, this appointment with the ENT set in place a whole series of appointments where we were given incorrect information. This resulted in our hopes being raised and then just as quickly being dashed, making for a rollercoaster of emotions.

Our first hurdle was to decipher whether or not Sian's hearing loss was from fluid in her ear or a sensori-neural loss. He suggested that a build-up of fluid in the ear could result in her level of hearing loss. This lack of hearing may have caused Sian to "switch off" from sound. We were given the chance to hope that the diagnosis was not a profound hearing loss as first thought and also that the cause of deafness was fluid in her ear and not a sensori-neural loss, meaning that with grommets inserted in each ear Sian would be able to hear. Naturally I clung to this hope like a limpet.

Subsequently, Sian had grommets put in and the ENT said Sian had responded to a bell in the recovery room and could hear the tinkle of the bells on her slippers. He said we should start to see a difference the next day—another false hope to cling to. Our GP said with chronic glue ear, the hearing nerve can shut down. He thought it would take a while for her hearing nerve and hearing to return. He even suggested that we not get Sian fitted with hearing aids.

I think of years later when Sian was 19 and had received her second cochlear implant. At her "switch on" she started crying as she was overcome with emotion. She couldn't see me to lipread, yet when I said, "What's wrong, darling?" she understood what I had said and was able to respond. She had worn a hearing aid in this ear until she was about eight in the hope that any residual hearing could be stimulated. Sian hated wearing the aid and stopped wearing it around this time. This ear had no access to sound for 11 years and what information she did receive through the hearing aid was miniscule. This refuted what the local ENT had said at the time of her diagnosis, that the brain would switch off from sound from lack of stimulation.

We had our first of many visits to the National Acoustics Laboratory (NAL), now Australian Hearing. Once again, Sian got a diagnosis of a profound hearing loss with a tiny corner audiogram. The ENT and GP were both still saying that the deafness could be due to the glue ear. NAL and Frankston Hospital audiologists were saying it was a sensori-neural loss. This was incredibly frustrating and confusing. We had been thrust into a world we knew nothing about, trying to make decisions with professionals giving vastly different opinions. I remember being totally overwhelmed with the options available. This led to our second hurdle of trying to work out whether or not Sian did indeed need hearing aids. Finally, she was fitted with hearing aids.

At the Royal Children's Hospital, we were told early on that it might be possible in the future for children who have lost their hearing at birth to have success with cochlear implants. But it was emphasised not to hang out for this possibility.

Choosing early intervention was directly linked to what form of communication we would choose for Sian. I began a gruelling round of visits to early intervention centres and spoke to the first of many parents of deaf children and adults who were deaf. What very quickly became apparent was that there were lots of conflicting views about the best form of communication for deaf children: from one end of the spectrum that supported Auslan as the best form of communication, through to signed English, cued speech and then the Auditory Verbal approach developed by a Canadian called Judy Simser. (In its purest form, the Auditory Verbal approach allows a child to develop speech and language by only using residual hearing with no lipreading while the mouth is covered.) Each professional had a different view on the possibility of Sian acquiring speech and language. Rereading my diary reminds me of what an awful time this was and how difficult it was to sift through conflicting information in order to make the best decision for Sian.

We finally decided on the John Pearce Centre (JPC). This was our third hurdle deciding on the communication style we would choose for Sian and the corresponding early intervention centre. JPC used the Auditory Verbal technique initially and could add in other communication systems as needed. I felt this was the best option to help Sian to learn to talk. We were a hearing family in a hearing world and my hope was that Sian would learn to talk. I was very impressed and felt that this would meet an important criterion for me, being that Sian's brothers could be involved in her early intervention program.

Very early on, Sister Joan Winter from JPC mentioned the possibility of Sian having a cochlear implant. The future was so unknown. No one could give a definite answer as to how this journey would look and how it would end. There were lots of questions, but no answers. My emotions were all over the place. One minute I felt strong; the next minute I felt like I couldn't cope. I felt angry. Why had life dealt us this? I hoped that slowly I would have a level of acceptance without anger or depression.

**25 July 1989.** About two months after the diagnosis we met Pam Dawson, an audiologist for the UoM's Cochlear Implant Clinic at the RVEEH led by Professor Clark. She went through Sian's audiograms and said there was a possibility that she would be a candidate for the implant.

**4 September 1989.** Sian had a test at the imaging department of Epworth Hospital. I was desperately hoping that this would indicate that she was a candidate for the cochlear implant. Pam Dawson called at about 2:45 pm and said the test was fine. She was medically and audiologically suitable for the implant. The decision was now up to us. I told her we were extremely keen and motivated and, of course, we wanted to go ahead. The ear with the least amount of hearing would have the implant. This was just four months since the initial diagnosis. If the option had been there to have the operation immediately, I would have jumped at the chance. There was still an element of uncertainty until close to the date of the operation about whether or not the operation would proceed. I found this nerve-wracking.

Sian's speech therapist at the Cochlear Implant Clinic, Louise Rowlands, said that there was no data on anyone in her position. This meant that no other child who was deaf from birth and who was as young as Sian had had an implant. She was a pioneer and was in a unique position. This prospect was both terrifying and exhilarating at the same time. The only assurance we had was that, at the very least, Sian would recognise some environmental sounds. The decision for Sian to have the implant required a huge leap of faith. From my point of view this was the only decision to make if my aim for her was that she acquire speech.

There was only a handful of children who had cochlear implants. They were all older and most had hearing at birth, their deafness being a result of medical conditions like rubella or meningitis. This meant that their experiences were different from Sian's. For some period of time they had heard, unlike Sian who had never been able to access speech. We were so lucky with the amount of support we received throughout this whole journey from JPC, the Cochlear Implant Clinic and NAL, who all worked together seamlessly to support both Sian and our whole family.

One of the most contentious issues we faced was the backlash from the Signing Deaf Community over parents choosing for their children to have cochlear implants. This was mainly comprised of deaf families who used Auslan as a means of communication. They felt very strongly over the following issues:

- Auslan signing is the natural language for deaf people.

- Deaf culture and language could end if deaf people could hear with cochlear implants.

- The implant is cruel. Parents are trying to make their deaf children an imitation of hearing people.

- It is your fate to be deaf. Just leave it as it is.

- Deaf children can make the decision to have an implant when they are older.

The problem with this view is that it is too late for people to learn useful speech at this age. The optimum time to learn speech is from birth to eight years.

One thing that really struck me about these views was that deaf adults seemed to think that they had a right to determine my child's future. As far as I knew there was no other disability group that held these views. As a parent I wanted what I considered to be the best option for my child and my family.

**20 October 1989.** After lots of testing, Pam Dawson said the results were confirmed, and Sian was definitely a candidate for the implant. I can still remember the sense of elation and hope I felt at this news. Our fourth hurdle had been overcome. Sian was a candidate for the cochlear implant.

**17 November 1989.** Louise Rowlands rang to say a date had been set for the implant: 13 March 1990. I was delighted. I would have jumped at the chance to have the operation then and there.

**1 December 1989.** Sian's case went before the Ethics Committee the day before and it was passed. Our fifth hurdle had been jumped. We visited the hospital ward at the RVEEH in Melbourne where the Cochlear Implant Clinic was located and where the surgery would take place. I wanted to acquaint Sian with the rooms and took photos to make a little book to view at home.

**27 February 1990.** We met Mr Pyman, Sian's surgeon, at the implant clinic. He said, "Let's hope we have many happy times ahead." He went through the risks of the operation. So far, they had performed 101 operations. I signed the consent form. An audiologist who was not from the clinic, whom I had not met before, suggested we postpone the implant because Sian had a slightly better reading at 500 Hz. I nearly cried. Thankfully I was told by another audiologist from the clinic, "The decision has been made. Sian will have the implant."

**11 March 1990.** Sian was admitted to the RVEEH in preparation for her operation.

**Sian Neame, aged two years, after her cochlear implant operation in 1990. She was born profoundly deaf in one ear and severely deaf in the other.**

**13 March 1990.** Finally, the day arrived. Professor Clark came in. It was the first time we had met. He was very concerned about Sian and thoroughly checked and questioned her observation chart. Thankfully, the operation was a success and all 22 electrodes were inserted. At two-and-a-half, Sian was the youngest pre-linguistically deaf child in Australia to receive a cochlear implant. A lot of publicity followed.

**15 March 1990.** A press conference was held in Sian's room, with newspapers, television and radio stations. What an experience. There were people, cameras, microphones and lights everywhere. Sian sat on the bed for two hours while photographs and interviews took place. She seemed to take it all in her stride.

An appearance on *Good Morning Australia* and an article in the *Woman's Day* magazine, to name a few, followed. I found this attention and that people were interested in Sian's journey quite therapeutic. It was challenging at times to know that my daughter looked different, wearing a body-worn speech processor and magnet on her head with long cables dangling from it. This was especially difficult straight after the operation when her head was shaved on the side of the implant. The speech processor and magnet were stark against her skin.

Two days after being released from hospital, Sian was admitted once again with an infection. This was a worrying time but luckily the issue resolved quickly.

**3 April 1990.** "Switch-on" day was the day that some of Sian's electrodes hopefully would be turned on. There were reporters and cameras everywhere. It took a long time to even get the magnet on Sian's head. It was a matter of trying to get her to respond to an electrical impulse. But this was a new experience for Sian, and it was hard to ascertain exactly what she was recognising. I remember feeling very agitated. I am sure Sian sensed this. It was decided after a couple of hours to send us home with the processor not working. Then we decided that we would come back after lunch. It was a very tense time. We spoke to the media to get rid of them. The hospital gave audio-visuals to the TV stations.

We were more relaxed, and Sian was more settled after a break. The audiologists were trying to determine the threshold for electrode 18. (The threshold is what you can just hear. At the other end is the comfort level, the level just below discomfort.) We stayed at the clinic until 3 pm. We were very tired and emotionally drained. As soon as we got home, we had a call from *Good Morning Australia* saying they would come to our home in Mount Martha to interview. It felt like we had been swept up in a whirlwind and were being carried along.

Thus continued an endless round of appointments at the Cochlear Implant Clinic in Melbourne, JPC in Ripponlea and NAL in Frankston. We lived in Mount Martha and so it was a lot of driving and time that was spent travelling to appointments. Added to this were numerous appointments at the emergency department of the RVEEH following up suspected ear infections. Sian did not have the language initially to tell us what was wrong and so there was a lot of guesswork. Often, I would get to the hospital to be told there was nothing wrong. A lot of unnecessary trips were made to the emergency department, but I was terrified that Sian would get an infection in her ear that would compromise the implant. It took quite a few months for all the electrodes to be turned on and set at the correct levels. This mapping continues to be done to this day. They make slight adjustments as needed and the plasticity of the brain accepts each new map with its slight alterations.

Over the following months Sian started reacting to sounds in her environment, sounds that previously she could not hear. Standing on Parliament Station, she heard a lady walking past wearing stilettos. She heard the train coming. When I was putting the Duplo away, Sian indicated I was making too much noise. She heard the whistle of a train. She reacted to the paint shaker in a paint shop. She heard the electric cash register.

Sian heard a toilet flushing. Each of these moments gave me hope that Sian would eventually achieve speech.

A major issue we had to deal with was the myriad of problems that could befall the speech processor, cables and magnets. This caused quite a lot of angst over the years. The Cochlear Implant Clinic was the only place where spare parts could be sourced or where technicians could fix the problem. Often there would be frantic calls between parents to try and source a spare part on the weekend. It was often a guessing game to try and work out what the problem was: a tri-cord cable could split, the speech processor case could break, one or both lights on the processor might stop working or the magnet case might split. The possibilities were endless.

The processor was charged by disposable batteries or rechargeable batteries, but they weren't always reliable in holding the necessary charge. Added to the mechanical issues that could beset the external components of the cochlear implant, a little toddler wearing this device was bound to take the speech processor and magnet on a number of adventures. Most memorable was the time they were taken for a swim in a pool. These days, there are waterproof covers to make this possible. It is only in the last few years that Sian has been able to experience hearing while being in water. The speech processor has developed over the years, and it is now a small, behind-the-ear device with a magnet. From Sian's current experiences, it seems to be less prone to breakdowns and is much more reliable. There are fewer external parts to break down.

I constantly monitored Sian's speech development and kept a daily speech diary until she was about eight.

**13 September 1991.** Sian's fourth birthday. I had recorded over 500 words that Sian could say.

The year after Sian's implant saw us involved in a number of media events. Professor Clark and I appeared on *Good Morning Australia* debating the benefits of a cochlear implant, especially for children. Sian had photos taken by *The Age* and was the face of the Deafness Foundation (DF) Telethon.

**5 September 1992.** During Sian's mapping session, she did not respond to electrode 7. I was devastated. I had become used to her not responding to sounds when doing audiograms, but to see Sian not responding now to an electrode, I couldn't believe it. It was real anguish. But electrode 8 would take over its work. Instead of sounds being cut up in 22 pieces, they would be slightly rearranged, and the sounds would now be divided between 21 electrodes. Each electrode would do slightly more work, like a breadstick being cut up into 21 pieces rather than 22 pieces. I was told it wouldn't make any difference. Now I had lost some confidence. Sian had been cheated once. At the next appointment, electrode 3 was lost as well. I had a very dramatic reaction when these electrodes no longer functioned, no doubt due to a lack of understanding of the process. I now realise it did not make any difference to what Sian could hear.

All these years later, I look in awe at where Sian is in her life now. She speaks beautifully and even now I notice any addition to her knowledge of words. Just recently she used the word "feisty" and I remember thinking, "Wow, that is amazing!" and, "I wonder where she picked that word up." We all laugh, including Sian, when she uses a word incorrectly. Occasionally, Sian will ask for the meaning of a word. She operates in both the hearing and deaf worlds, having learned to sign Auslan in her teens. She would like to develop this skill to make herself more proficient in Auslan. She is married to Matt and is the loving mother of Mihaela who, as I write this, is 14 months old. Sian talks to her incessantly, being very aware of the importance of developing speech and language. I look on in awe at Mihaela's speech development. I wonder how I could have missed that Sian was not hearing, and therefore mute. At home Sian has music playing in the background so that Mihaela will experience the joy of music, something that is not especially familiar to Sian. This is in stark contrast to when she was growing up, as I tried to limit the amount of background noise to create an optimum listening environment. Sian is teaching Mihaela baby sign even though she is hearing, and this process is fascinating. Her little chubby hands try to mimic Sian. Her first signs were "dog" and "sit."

Sian has completed a degree in Interior Design (with Honours). She is currently working as an interior designer in Melbourne. She thoroughly enjoys the process of spatial planning and designing the interiors of buildings.

Sian has had the opportunity to be involved in a number of exciting media events, including making a presentation to the wife of the Prime Minister of the Netherlands at the BEI in Mollison House, and at an annual fundraising dinner for the BEI, 11 November 1997.

## Sian's recollections

My childhood was my normalcy. I knew no different. It was what it was. Sure, I had wished for different things such as less appointments and ears that worked exactly the same as my brothers' and friends'.

I remember it seemed like there were constant visits to the RVEEH for appointments, and I remember the taste and smell of melted Vegemite sandwiches after what seemed like a long trip to the city from our home on the Peninsula. I would get so grumpy sometimes that Mum would have to bribe me with a treat from the kiosk. The Mars bars had never tasted so good.

I liked the listening games with the friendly audiologists, and at the time we knew a lot of faces. This made the draining appointments fun and it helped make the time go fast. Being a perfectionist, I strived for perfect results from listening tests. I wanted to please everyone and myself. I would focus so hard on each sound and letter to the point that I would be tired out each evening.

I vividly remember that everyone would stare at me in public, especially the super-market, and Mum would tell me to ignore them or stare back. This made me self-conscious. I didn't understand why they were staring at me. I knew I had a magnet on my head, but I didn't think it was such a big deal. When I was much younger, if I saw someone up at the shops with the implant it was most likely someone I knew from school. Now, I see so many more people with the implants and no one makes a big deal out of it. I often have the urge to go and say, "Hi." It is always nice to see someone else with a cochlear implant. It is like we are connected in some way, in a big extended family. It is great that there is more awareness about cochlear implants these days, and they seem to be socially accepted.

I remember the constant media attention and interviews. There was a time when we had the media turn up to our home, and I don't think I had realised what was about to happen. I was so over it that I threw the biggest tantrum. I had had enough of the attention. I just wanted to be a kid. The older I became, the more I appreciated my cochlear implant and what it has done for me. So I would do anything to help share my story.

I was very fortunate to have been able to attend mainstream school and play with hearing children. There were only a few of us hearing-impaired kids at St Mary's (a facility for hearing-impaired students), and so it allowed us to broaden our friend-ships and experiences. We would play "taggy" and "What's the time, Mr Wolf?" The kids accepted me for who I was. They didn't know I was any different. High school was different. Teenagers from different schools who had not had any experience with people who were deaf would notice your "impairment." Being deaf is not an impairment.

I remember in grade 5 I had a teacher who didn't understand why I needed extra support because I had really good hearing. She was a bit difficult to deal with. When I was growing up, some people had this misunderstanding that I had perfect hearing because I could hear so well and they didn't understand why I needed extra support. Extra support meant filling in the gaps of what I could potentially miss out in conver-sation or instructions from the teacher. Listening can be tiring, because hearing-impaired people have to work a lot harder than hearing people to listen, but I don't think people understand the strenuous effort that is involved. I found this particularly hard at university. I don't think my university peers could understand why I had a note-taker who would follow me around even though I could hear and speak. I was less able to build solid friendships.

Dancing, listening to music and creating my own performances are some of my best childhood memories that hearing children also have. Although I cannot sing, I was still

**Sian Neame with surgeon Brian Pyman at the launch of *Sounds from Silence* at the Bionic Ear Institute.**

accepted and created fun memories. Bless those ears around me.

In order to help me feel that I fitted in, my mum would cleverly sew harnesses and holes in pockets for my cables so that my processor was hidden out of sight. I remember getting frustrated with the long cable to my processor, especially on hot days when it would cling to my sweat. I hated anything sticking to me. I had always dreamt of a cableless processor. I was so delighted when this was finally released when I started high school. It came at a perfect time. It helped to make me feel a bit less different.

Batteries, batteries, batteries. Always had to have a spare. It'd be hell without them, otherwise. There was an age when I wanted to make this strenuous time of changing batteries more fun, when it was something I had no choice but to deal with. I would do a prank on myself. I'd change my battery and put the flat batteries in the battery packet. To me it was funny at the time. It wasn't so funny when I needed the battery. I had to entertain myself somehow.

I would sit with my back to the fire and I would be reminded not to get my processor too hot. There were times I would accidentally get my processor wet. There was a time when I was playing in the backyard with the garden hose and I would put it up in the air, and of course a big blob of water would come crashing down on my processor. Another vivid memory is when I had a hearing friend over to play. We hopped into the pool and all of a sudden, I couldn't hear. I realised I was too busy talking and listening to remember to take my processor off. I tried drying off the processor in the oven with no luck. The play date was cut short and off we went to the RVEEH to get it fixed.

As much as I enjoyed going to the beach and pools with family and friends, I would often find this exhausting, not being able to hear and having to rely on lipreading. I was so excited when the Aqua+ waterproof cover for the processor was released. I am still getting my head around the fact that I can hear in the water.

## Isaac McMullen
## A typical child implanted at a young age (2004)

When Isaac McMullen came to my attention with a profound hearing loss, I was already amazed by the speed at which children's language could develop when they had an implant from a very young age. I felt it best for us to undertake Isaac's implant at the Royal Children's Hospital, as their staff had more experience in using anaesthetics with his age group. That situation has now changed, as the RVEEH has excellent staff and facilities for this age group.

## Isaac McMullen's story

Isaac's mother writes:

> Words: they have power—they hold life and death. In the beginning the Word created the world, putting into motion light and the heavens and all creation. This was always strongly instilled into me as a child. I suppose that is what underpinned my understanding of the depth and width of language and the loss of it. Isaac Jacob McMullen, born 2002, diagnosed at seven months. Unilaterally implanted at 22 months and bilaterally implanted at 14 years of age.
>
> It was my favourite time of the year. It was Christmas Eve. The sun was strong and had that familiar summer sting to it. I could smell hot tinsel as it sat glittering on the windowsill. It reminded me of the Christmases I had had in the past as a young girl. It has always been my favourite time of year—I love the traditions, the festivities and the family celebrations. But not that Christmas in 2002. It was the hardest Christmas ever.

My great-aunt was a deaf teacher, and over the years her students and her passion for giving children the gift of speech had been impressed on me. I had seen for myself the struggles of these deaf students. Their primitive grunts and tones as they tried to communicate seemed to frustrate them and frightened me as a child. This was how they communicated. They seemed alone with a language they used with their hands that both intrigued me and made me wary. I was quite aware that only one person in that room could adequately understand the thoughts and comments that they were trying to convey. My great-aunt knew Auslan, a method of communication that used exaggerated facial expressions and hand gestures that made sense to those who knew it, but not to those who did not. Aunty Gwen was the only one able to tell us what her guests wanted and what they had said. To me it was both saddening and charming at the same time.

My aunt was a strong, squat and a very determined lady. She never married and was happy to chat about her "family" that was the deaf students she adored so much. I found myself by her side listening to tales of her students over and over. I was intrigued though slightly bored with her stories, but nevertheless, no one else would listen to her and so I did. Little did I know that these anecdotes would be the foundation and framework of the biggest gift of life to both myself and my son. God used these stories and words. They settled in my heart and into my young mind, which prepared for the journey ahead many years later.

As I sat in the audiologist reception, with my seven-month-old baby on my knee, listening to the soft melody of *Silent Night* in the background, it crossed my mind, "What if, in fact, my little baby had silent nights since the day he was born? What if …?" And in those moments, a thousand thoughts and memories flooded my mind. A familiar voice spoke so softly, reassuring me that it would be all right no matter what. My mum's voice has always been so comforting. I heard his name: Isaac McMullen. A young, tall, solemn man called from the reception. I hesitantly stood with my mother by my side, my son alert, looking around and taking everything in. I took a deep breath, said a quick prayer, and held that breath for an instant, then walked through the doors.

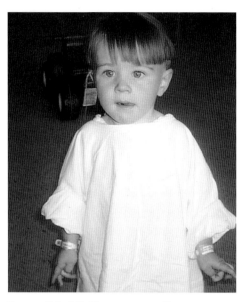

**Isaac McMullen soon after his implant at the Royal Children's Hospital.**

The beeps, the ones they test hearing with, got louder and louder—my son was not even twinging at the noises that filled the room, noises that I could hear through the headphones that had been placed on both my mother and me to protect our hearing. Mickey Mouse turned around on a stick as if to mock me as the sounds increased, and my mind tried to process just what was happening. I glanced at my mum, who gave me the look that says, "It's okay. We will get through this." I could feel the tears trying to erupt, but the strength of faith gently saying that nothing happens that God hasn't ordained.

"Mrs McMullen, your son is profoundly deaf. He will need hearing aids and may need a cochlear implant. Merry Christmas." With that we were directed to the exit, and the world from that moment on was forever changed.

That Christmas I saw my aunt cry for the first time ever. I felt her intensity as she tightly held my arms and begged me to give Isaac a voice. She said, "Stop at nothing, not until he speaks. Promise me! Promise me that!" This she said over and over fervently. Staring straight into her eyes as she said this, and then watching her emotions while she looked down at the audiogram that had been handed to me the day before, I knew this would be the most serious of promises that I could make for my son. To me, this audiogram was a mess of lines and crosses reminding me of my days at school with maths. It was just a graph, but to Aunty Gwen it was a life sentence for my baby boy. She had seen firsthand just how much impact this could have on all of our lives.

I was restless that night. I had gone through the motions of applying for a cochlear implant and we were denied. I didn't understand why. It seemed simple to me. My son needed one and this denial was not an option. I picked up my Bible and I searched for the words to give me guidance. I looked to God for some inspiration, flicking through the pages, as if I was preparing for some kind of divine intervention to put my mind and heart at rest. Frustrated, I turned on the radio beside me and listened to a Christian station, hoping for some extreme guidance. That night, God answered me in a true and direct way. On this particular evening, at this precise moment, I listened to an interview by the man who invented the cochlear implant. I heard Professor Clark speaking about why and how he had created the cochlear implant. It was like every word he said came straight for my hearing. I couldn't believe it. I heard his voice like it was a direct line to me. It was both surreal and true, reaching me all at once. It cemented what I knew I had to do. I had to find a way to implant my child. "No" was not an option. I had a fire in my heart, a determination to hear the words my son would indeed one day say. I was on a mission from God and I now knew it.

As I dialled, I practised the words: "Professor Clark, you don't know me. But God wants my son implanted and I need your help." They seemed ridiculous and feeble in my mind, but how else was I to make sense to anyone what I had felt? That day, I spoke with Professor Clark's personal assistant. I'm sure she was confused at what she heard over that phone line, but she politely took my name and address. True to her word, she passed on the information. In the weeks to follow, a letter signed by Professor Clark himself arrived offering advice. This was the beginning of a journey and as a family, we will forever be grateful for it.

Isaac was implanted when he was 22 months old, and on this day our prayers were answered. Hope was surgically placed into my little boy's head and his future was sealed with 22 electrodes covered in silicon. Two weeks later, at "switch on," in a room just like the one Isaac was diagnosed in, I could feel my heart race. I said silent prayers like those on the day he was diagnosed. I stepped into that sound booth, which had an eerie resemblance to the booth we sat in when Isaac was diagnosed. I could see a puppet turning on a stick, just like the one that Christmas Eve. Tears were welling up.

"He's on air!" And with that, Isaac threw himself back on his little chair laughing and pointing at the silly duck puppet as it rotated. He heard noises for the first time through his cochlear implant. All 22 electrodes were turned on and working.

No longer will there be silent nights. A sigh of relief, and a "Thank you, God," as together we took on the years that followed. Within six months, Isaac had learned over 100 words. We made everything a speech lesson and looked for new things to learn. Each day, he exploded with sounds and words that delighted not only us but his great-great-aunt Gwen. Her tears were now of joy.

Aunty Gwen said her life's work had been completed with that small voice that came from Isaac. A profoundly deaf boy's words ushered her into the presence of God with eternal rest, her purpose completed. Her charge was for Isaac to carry her work on, to let people know that deaf kids can talk.

Isaac is the youngest of my four boys. He has been able to follow them to mainstream schools and has achieved grades equal to that of his hearing brothers. I have watched him "hear" life with different ears from mine. He hears better; he hears with his heart. He understands that the loud chirp of a cicada is something to enjoy, whereas to us it can be plain annoying. Living in the suburbs all of my life, I had always known the cicadas' song and took it for granted, but now I understand its brilliance. Isaac has taught us that every sound is a gift and makes up the mosaic of life.

If sounds are placed together, they make a tune that can be anything from a symphony to a simple schoolyard ditty. Sounds can serve as a warning of approaching cars or the fire bell that is essential in our fire-prone suburb. It's the wind that whips through the trees, the clap of thunder as it accompanies a majestic lightning show, the purr of a pet cat wanting attention, or the bark of a dog excited to welcome you home.

So, a cochlear implant is freedom—it gives choices for life. It has given my son a future in any industry of his gifting. It has released him from the silence he was born into, and given him hope and trust in a beautiful, melodic future.

Having Isaac implanted really was an easy choice, but how to manage it was more difficult. There was a strong culture against implantation, and definitely against having an oral child. We still are confronted with this as we navigate life, but we hold true to our choices and hope that Isaac's life can inspire others to see the freedom and the chances an implant can provide.

Isaac said to me only a couple of years ago that he felt that if words were powerful enough to create the universe, to have the power of life and death in the tongue, then it is of the utmost importance that children are given the voice they deserve, and that children are implanted. Isaac now understands for himself what his life could have been and just how different it would have been.

What is a cochlear implant? Well, it's watching a little grandchild speak to his 102-year-old grandma. It's seeing Isaac stand with a youth choir singing his heart out, or listening to him play the violin, correcting the notes as he goes, realising that it is a little too flat. It's hearing me yell from the kitchen to the backyard that dinner is ready, being at a friend's house for a play and the friend's mother having no idea that Isaac is deaf, calling out to the boys to stop fighting and blaming the wrong child because they sound so alike, walking into a mainstream school with the only profoundly deaf child and watching him call out to all his friends, seeing him order an iced chocolate for himself for the first time, watching him play Marco Polo in the pool with his brothers, seeing him play PlayStation with his friends, waving him goodbye on school wilderness camps with no power (but thankful for disposable batteries), watching him driving off with an instructor for his first driving lesson, listening to him plan his subjects for university, asking for a second implant (bilateral), watching him talk with Professor Clark and seeing the bond and the moments God has brought together, seeing others see in Isaac the possibilities and hope for their deaf children, learning that a child we have never met can now speak because her parents saw Isaac on television, and had their daughter implanted. It's what the future can hold for Isaac, not how we can make a future for him.

Deep within sound are the gifts from God: the call of the bird, the sound of friends laughing together, the choir in a church singing a hymn of years past. Voice is a unique aspect of a person. If I close my eyes, I can still hear the sweet sound of my grandma talking to me in my memories, I can hear my mother's words comfort me, and now I can hear my son say, "I love you, Mum," "Mum, where's my uniform?" "Hey Mum, I want to be an ambassador for Cochlear Ltd, to give kids a chance like me." All of these are as unique as a fingerprint, and all of these imprint your heart eternally.

Now at nearly 17, Isaac has appeared on television, addressed Parliament, sung in choirs and had speaking parts in school productions. He's been fully mainstreamed in both primary and secondary schools, being the only deaf child in primary and in his secondary school. Isaac can swim and play water games with his friends with the attachments that come with his processors. Isaac is above average in his grades and is even being elevated this year in a subject. He has led a church service, spoken to renowned people from all over the world, taken on the violin and piano, but most of all he can communicate with whomever he wants. He can even play online games, talking to his friends over the internet while playing on his PlayStation 4. This is without seeing their faces—all by listening alone. Wow!

**"I want to help Professor Clark. I want to give deaf kids a voice." Isaac McMullen and Graeme at the Graeme Clark Oration in 2018 at the Melbourne Convention Centre.**

A cochlear implant is a gift of life, a gift of communication. It's putting the colour back into a black-and-white world. It's new each day and it makes sense. It's communication. It's living in the wider community. It's life to the fullest for Isaac. It is his future. Isaac has a voice. (And yes, in case you are wondering, you couldn't even tell he is deaf by his voice.) He has a purpose; he has the words; he has hope and faith. Isaac has a plan, and that is to help others have a voice as he does. "Mum, I want to help Professor Clark. I want to give deaf kids a voice like mine." This is the biggest gift a cochlear implant has given my son—a purpose and a plan.

My prayers are more than answered, my hopes more than fulfilled, my heart more than filled and my gratitude will never be enough. A cochlear implant to me is essential for mental health; for living to the fullest. Bless you, Professor Clark, for hearing God, so my son can hear God.

## BAR TO THE M.C.

Lt. R. B. ASHCROFT, M.C., Notts and Derby R., Spec. Res., R.F.C.—For conspicuous gallantry and devotion to duty in ing enemy troops from an extremely low altitude; on on he attacked from the rear from a height of about 150 emy that were holding up our infantry.

Sec. Lt. A. C. YOUDALE, M.C., spicuous gallantry and devotion to d from an extremely low altitude. from the rear, from a height of abo holding up our infantry.

# CHAPTER TWO

# Family background

My forebears have influenced me indirectly with values for life. I have been close to some and seen their challenges, successes and failures. I have wondered what I would have done in similar circumstances with a mixture of their genes. I also valued the Christian tradition some have passed on and decided my emphases in life should be God, wife, family and then work.

## My father's forebears

The Clark side has been traced to the 16th century from the records of Old Aberdeen Scotland by the New Spalding Club. They are recorded as being primarily burgesses and merchants. William, my great-grandfather, arrived in Melbourne around 1855, went to the Victorian gold-fields and opened three stores around Newstead. His store and house are still there today. He was well-known and liked for his compassionate attitude to the unfortunate. For example, as narrated by Colin Clark, one night he was held up by bushrangers:

> The moonlight filtered through the trees, illuminating the road as it wound its way along the slopes of the mountain, leading towards shelter and the comforts of home. All that was heard on this still night was the steady beat of the horses' hooves as they propelled the four-wheeled caravan towards its destination. With the reins held loosely in his hands, the 14-stone, 5' 7" passenger alternately dozed and wakened as the conveyance encountered from time to time the rough patches of potholes that marked the road. Suddenly the scene changed, the horses reared, and the driver came to life as two horsemen appeared, their faces masked and guns in their hands. With a rough demand for money and gold, one of them approached the van while the other

**Captain Alfred Youdale and his observer showing off the AA damage to their 9 squadron RE8 in September 1917.**

**Colin with his mother Millie, brother Ernie, his father Alfred and brother Alan circa 1915.**

kept his firearm levelled at the occupant. Just then, the moonlight showed the features of the passenger as he sat bolt upright in his seat, and the highway man said to his companion, "It is Clark of Newstead." With an oath the other man replied: "Let him go!" and they rode off into the dense bush at the side of the road. Such was the reputation of this man in the surrounding district for his compassion and help to the needy.[5]

When the goldfields failed, William lost all his money. He then moved to Melbourne and started to import goods into Australia. But in competition with the big companies, his business collapsed. Their eldest son Alfred William, my grandfather, had to take a lot of responsibility for bringing up the family.

My father lived with his parents Alfred William and Amelia, and older brothers Ernest and Alan over their shop at 6 High Street, St Kilda, and then at 7 Emilton Avenue, St Kilda.

## My father: Colin Milbourne Clark

My father was born on 27 December 1905 at St Kilda, Melbourne where he spent his childhood. Dad comments in his memoirs that he only came alive at 12 years, and for the years 1918 to 1922 his father paid for him to go to Scotch College, one of Melbourne's so-called great public schools which we would now call private schools. Dad wanted to do medicine and be a pathologist, but his father could not afford it. He chose pharmacy and graduated in second place. The Great Depression was about to start and jobs were hard to find. After one unsatisfactory position, a friend told him there might be an opening for a pharmacy in Stroud, NSW.

In reflection, he writes:

> I caught the train to Stroud (population 400) and arrived in the middle of the night. The next morning, when I saw how small the town was, I decided to leave straight away but could not get a train out. The locals, however, wanted me to stay and persuaded me to buy the newsagency and combine it with a pharmacy.

**Colin Clark at the junction of the Pinch River and the Snowy River.**

So Dad started the first pharmacy in Stroud, which saw him through the Depression and enabled him to earn £10 a week. Here, he met my mother Dorothy Thomas when she came to visit. It had been her home for a few years while her father was the principal of the school.

## My mother's forebears

On my mother's paternal side, William Thomas (aged 48) and his wife Mary Thomas (aged 50) left their farm, *Skillegate*, in St Keverne, Cornwall, in October 1848 as times were hard. Together with five of their children they made their way to Portsmouth and sailed on the *Harbinger* direct to Sydney, arriving in Australia on 12 February 1849.[6] William and his family were heartbroken when one of their sons died unexpectedly. They resolved to start a new life by crossing the Blue Mountains to the western farming lands beyond. It took them seven days by coach to reach the top of Mount Victoria, aware they could be attacked by bushrangers and convicts. They then had to make the perilous journey down the other side and travel via Bathurst to the Cornish settlement at Guyong, just east of the expanding town of Orange.

**Four of the five Youdale boys went to World War I. In the front row (left to right) are Percy and Stan, and behind them (left to right) are Eric, Roy and Alfred.**

At an auction sale in Orange on 29 October 1860, William Thomas made his first purchase of land and named it *Hillview*, as it became known to us. His eldest son was my grandfather George Edmund Thomas (1874–1961), who became a primary school teacher in Sydney. There he met my grandmother Lucy May Youdale (1877–1950). *Hillview* remained in the family and I have fond memories of holidays there picking pears, learning to milk cows and to drive the tractor. (Years later I had visions of practising as an ENT specialist in Orange, which had become a beautiful city.)

On my grandmother Lucy May's side, I am descended from John Small and Mary Parker, who arrived in Australia from Birmingham and London respectively on the *Charlotte* and *Lady Penryn* in the First Fleet. John Small was from the Edgbaston quarter of Birmingham, UK. As a young man he sought adventure by joining the marines, went to sea on *HMS Lively* and engaged in combat with the Americans. He was finally discharged jobless by the British navy. He and three others decided to hold up a squire and steal his watch and some cash. They were caught and tried at the Exeter assizes by visiting judges from London. Only one of the four was sentenced to hang, but John was sent on the long and dangerous journey on the First Fleet to Australia.

Mary Parker lived and worked in London as a domestic servant. She was charged for stealing two tablecloths and held in prison for six months. After release, she was accused of entering her former mistress' house and suspected of preparing to steal her washing. There was no substantial evidence for this, but she was sentenced to be transported to "parts beyond the seas."[7]

John Small and Mary Parker were married by Chaplain Richard Johnson, on 12 October 1788, probably under a gum tree at Farm Cove. In 1848 one of their grandsons Robert Small married Eliza Rebecca Hughes who was still alive in 1917 when my mother was a teenager. By then their daughter Rebecca Small had married John Beaumont Youdale and had a family of 13 living in Ashfield. Their eldest daughter Lucy May Youdale was my

**My maternal grandparents Lucy May and George Edmund Thomas in 1938.**

grandmother. She remembers her mother would sometimes get so harassed she would walk out and catch a tram, leaving Lucy May in charge.

Four of their sons, my great-uncles Alfred, Eric, Roy and Stan, went to Gallipoli, and the diaries of Alf and Eric are in the Australian War Memorial.

Alfred is considered the war hero of our family. He was shot down and killed flying over Belgium. He first fought for eight months in the Gallipoli campaign before being repatriated home with dysentery. Soon after recovering, he returned to the Western Front and trained as a pilot for the Royal Flying Corps, as Australia did not have a vacancy. His training was in Egypt for an hour a day over six days.

He flew many missions over German lines and was shot down eight times before a fatal ninth time on 23 December 1917. His exploits were described frequently by his commanding officer and in press articles.

In a letter of 18 October 1917, General Sir A. J. Godley from the Second Anzac Corps headquarters wrote to another general:

I should be glad if you would convey to the 21st Squadron my thanks and appreciation of the good work they did for us during our three battles. The reports given me by Youdale were especially valuable and accurate.

In *Art Obs* in 1918 the writer comments:

In my mind, Alfred Clarence Youdale will always be numbered among the flying aces of the First World War.[8]

**In 2019 at the Australian War Memorial with my four-year old grandson Alfred Clark, who is Alfred Youdale's great-great-great-nephew, viewing his military cross.**

For his exploits, Alfred received the Military Cross and Two Bars. The Military Cross was awarded for an act or acts of exemplary gallantry during active operations against the enemy. His medals became the property of his younger brother, Roy Youdale, who also flew many missions over France, and who spent most of his life in London. Before he died, he dispatched Alfred's medals back to my uncle Keith Thomas on the P&O ss *Himalaya*, which arrived in Sydney on 10 October 1969. However the medals were lost in transit. It was not until 2013 that we heard they were being looked after by the Russell RSL Club in New Zealand. After I found records showing they were sent but did not arrive in Australia (in the Keith Thomas/Graeme Clark Collection in Mitchell Library, Sydney), the New Zealand authorities generously agreed to give them to Australia for the War Memorial. Dr Brendan Nelson arranged at a special ceremony on 22 October 2019 to receive them from the New Zealand High Commissioner, Dame Annette King. Our four-year-old grandson Alfred was over-awed. There was much interest and appreciation for the work of the director Dr Brendan Nelson AO.

My grandmother Lucy May Thomas (née Youdale), the eldest in the Youdale family, had the responsibility of helping to raise her younger brothers and sisters, including Alfred and Roy. Lucy May was gifted at languages but could not pursue her studies beyond Sydney Girls High School because of family duties.

I remember my grandmother with a great deal of affection, as a loving, wise person. I cherish the year I spent with her in 1947 while I attended Sydney Boys High School. Because of her gift for languages, she would also help me with my French homework.

## My mother: Dorothy May Thomas

My mother, Dorothy May Thomas, was born on 20 May 1906 in Mosman, NSW. She showed a real love for music at an early age, and when walking around the streets would cling to the front fence of houses where there was

**Dorothy Thomas
in April 1930.**

music playing. On 16 March 1911, she had the joy of welcoming into the family a brother, Keith, with whom she was close all her life. Then, in 1913 her father was appointed as headmaster of the primary school in Stroud, NSW where she was able to expand her musical and artistic talents. She developed skills in sight-reading music and a love of painting.

When her father was moved to Kyogle in northern NSW she was attending Methodist Ladies' College (MLC) in Burwood and stayed in Ashfield at the Youdale home with her great-grandmother, grandparents, two aunts and three orphan cousins whose parents died in the flu pandemic of 1919.

From 1925, she and her family lived in a house they called *Marlborough* at 86 Auburn Street, Sutherland, which is now listed as a heritage house. With a scholarship in painting, Dorothy was able to attend the Sydney Art School (also known as the Julian Ashton School) along with such students as George Lambert and William Dobell.

**Colin Clark married Dorothy May Thomas at Malvern Hill Methodist Church on 28 November 1933.**

By now the Great Depression was approaching. Dorothy obtained work with a city firm doing shorthand, typing and bookkeeping, and then a second job playing the piano at Clifton Gardens at night on the other side of Sydney Harbour. This meant catching the ferry in all weathers before the last train at night to Sutherland, where the lonely figure of her father would be waiting to escort her home.

She was finally due for a holiday, but when several other plans fell through, she ended up going back to Stroud where her father had taught and where her family had friends. One evening, she was asked to accompany a visiting violinist at a recital in the Collins' home and was escorted back to her friend's house by two gentlemen, one of whom was Colin Clark. So began a romance that led to engagement in 1930, a wedding in 1933 and a life-long marriage.

Mum and Dad spent the rest of their lives in Camden, becoming involved in many different organisations and contributing to the life of the community. We children were blessed to have such loving and caring parents. Neither sought praise, but my sister and I are proud of the many things they did. A tribute to both was published in the *Sydney Morning Herald* on 21 May 2002.

Colin and Dorothy came to Camden, NSW as newlyweds in 1934. Colin associated himself with numerous organisations and sporting groups including Rotary, the Carrington Hospital board, Camden School Parents & Citizens, the Masonic Lodge, cricket, golf, lawn bowls and the Camden Historical Society. He was the Camden

**Clark family in 1950: Robin (12 years), Colin, Bruce (5 years), Dorothy and Graeme (15 years).**

Historical Society's president in the late 1960s and worked with Camden Council and the Rotary Club to acquire a room for a museum at the rear of the old Camden School of Arts building, which is now the Camden Library. The Camden Museum opened in 1970 and Colin continued his enthusiasm for and encouragement of the growth of the museum until his death 32 years later. Colin was a charming man with an unusual combination of interests and abilities. He had a deep Christian faith and a sense of humour that would often see a quirky side to events. He loved nature, was widely read and enjoyed a discussion on many issues. His life was celebrated recently at a memorial service at the Camden Uniting Church. Dorothy was a member of the hospital auxiliary, the Country Women's Association branch and the Red Cross, and was a noted local pianist and painter. She played for the local musicals and accompanied visiting violinists. She received numerous prizes for her water colour paintings at city shows.[9]

My sister Robin remembers:

Mum always wanted things done quickly and was quick herself. This tendency overlay a great deal of nervous energy which we probably inherited. A lot of Mum's community work was to help Dad's business, but she showed great feeling towards the underdog, the widowed and people living alone. Talking socially for long periods tired Mum out, partly because Dad's deafness meant she had to lead the conversation. She had a great sense of fun and remembered many stories. She also taught us to respect others' feelings—to always say something positive about others or nothing at all.

## My sister: Robin Beverley Clark

When I was just three years of age, my mother was due to have a second child and I was sent to stay with grandparents Lucy May and George Edmund Thomas. When Robin started to grow up at three or four years of age, she became a good companion and was allowed to participate in the imaginative games with me and our friend Ken Whiteman. To our shame, we tried to get her caught in traps we made, but she was too smart for that. Robin also enjoyed the freedom of growing up in a small country town and being able to ride her bike wherever she wished. For her secondary education she became a boarder at MLC, Burwood. Robin was a good student

**With Robin at 62 John Street, Camden, in 1943.**

and decided to follow in the footsteps of her father to become a pharmacist. Later, she met her husband Brian Taylor in Bendigo and they had four children, Andrew, Kathryn, Bronwyn and Graeme.

# My brother: Bruce Edmund Clark

Just after World War II ended in 1945, I remember sitting at the dining room table at 62 John Street, Camden, when our parents told Robin and me that we would have a baby brother or sister. Robin hoped for a sister and I hoped for a brother. I won the lottery. He was born at Matron Heize's Maternity Hospital in Camden and named Bruce because of our Scottish history and Edmund after his grandfather Thomas. Since he was 10 years younger, I treated him more like a son than a brother and we did much together even though I was away many hours at boarding school.

Later, as he grew, we played golf and went on walks in the Blue Mountains of NSW. He was most generous with his time and money, trained as a pharmacist to help my father and married Robyn Gallard. They had four children, Adrian, Robert, Janice and Elisabeth.

All too quickly, a day came in 2000 when we were on a walk and he could not eat a sandwich. That was the start of a sad and difficult journey as his bowel cancer progressed. I did as I had been doing for all members of my family and played an intermediary role in

**With my son Jonathan, and Bruce with his son Adrian in 1979.**

his management. Sadly, he died in February 2001, which was even more tragic for my father who was still alive. My mother had died in 1987.

## My wife: Margaret Rose Burtenshaw

**Margaret Burtenshaw, 1940.**

The central figure in our family has been my wife, Margaret Rose. Her father Frederick Leonard Burtenshaw (1901–1994) was an only child who came to Australia with his parents Harry and Leonora (née Tee) from Little Hampton, Sussex, England in 1912. Margaret's mother, Rose Hewson (1897–1956) was the youngest of a family of seven who had come by steamship to NSW in 1882 from Nosterfield, Yorkshire, England. Rose's father Thomas married Mary Learoyd (probably of Huguenot origin), set up as a builder in North Auburn and built the Methodist church there. The families on both sides were Methodist.

Margaret grew up in Burwood, NSW, with her loving mother and devoted father who taught Latin for 33 years at Fort Street Boys' High School. She has an older brother Leonard, who became the organist and choirmaster of two city Presbyterian churches and was head of music education at the Sydney Conservatorium for over 25 years.

Classical music was always heard in one form or another in their house, and when I was courting Margaret I was usually invited to sit and appreciate one of her father's records, like a Beethoven symphony.

For her secondary education Margaret attended MLC in Burwood and went on to study Arts, majoring in English and History at the University of Sydney (UoS). She repeated her first year after interrupting the course to care for her dear mother who was dying of breast cancer in 1956. She finished at the end of 1960 with first-class honours in English. Her English ability has been most useful to me in writing up my earlier PhD thesis, *Sounds from Silence*, and this book.

# CHAPTER THREE

# From childhood to medical graduate

I was born at 62 John Street, Camden, NSW, on 16 August 1935 and lived there until I was 10 years of age.

I was learning what life was like for a father who was severely deaf. As a five-year-old, when asked by my kindergarten teacher what I wanted to do when I grew up, I said, "I want to fix ears." Many years later, I was fortunate to reconnect with that teacher, when she visited my office at the Bionic Ear Institute (BEI) in 2000.

When I was old enough, I was allowed into the pharmacy to help make up prescriptions and even do some experiments, which earned me the title "Bunsen burner boy." Dad also let me see how he examined people's eyes and explained different conditions. I could see that customers were embarrassed when they asked for confidential items and Dad would say, "Speak up!"

Growing up in this small country town of 3,000 people, I could freely ride my bike along the often-unmade roads, wander off to explore the beauty of nature, or sit under a gum tree and just think. For a birthday party, my preference was to go to a paddock in Cobbitty or by the Nepean River at "Little Sandy" and play imaginative games with friends around the fallen logs and along bush tracks.

Various sports interested me, and I practised batting at cricket, using Donald Bradman's book to guide me. With an aptitude for high jump, I would practise in the backyard over a self-made high jump, until I slipped and ricked my neck. This accident later troubled me as an ENT surgeon, when I had to turn and twist to look up the nooks and crannies of noses and sinuses. Finishing my primary schooling a year younger than my contemporaries had both positive and negative effects for my later education, but 24 years later it was vital in allowing me to be qualified in time to take up the Chair of Otolaryngology at the University of Melbourne (UoM).

**My father Colin Clark in his pharmacy, Argyle Street, Camden, NSW, in 1945.**

**62 John Street, Camden, NSW,
where I was born.**

To help me choose a career my father sought professional advice. After the usual aptitude test, I was informed I could do medicine, but I was told I should consider a new discipline emerging in the 1940s called electronic engineering. However, when I read *The Life of Pasteur* by René Vallery-Radot and *Madame Curie* by her daughter Eve, I became inspired by the beauty and simplicity of their experiments in biology and physics. This lit a fire in the belly that I too might make discoveries in the biomedical and biophysical areas. So, I commenced doing chemical and biological experiments in my father's shop and mother's laundry, studying the diseases affecting the tomatoes in my garden, along with exploring crystal radios with my friend Fred Skinner.

At 11 years of age, when I decided to study medicine with encouragement from my father and uncle Keith Thomas, I had to leave Camden. The town that had moulded my life had no high school. Sydney Boys High School accepted me, and I lived in the city within easy travelling distance. I boarded all week with my grandmother Lucy May and grandfather George Edmund Thomas in a flat in Coogee, a seaside suburb of Sydney, and returned each Friday to Camden by steam train.

To catch the tram from Coogee to Sydney Boys High at Moore Park was a novel experience. The old "toast rack" trams had running boards for the conductor to walk along to collect the fares, and if he lost his grip he would be left behind. In that case we would have to wait until he caught up by running from the last stop! We also had even older trams referred to as "jumping jacks." The boys would get on the back and jump up and down to make the little tram actually bounce along the line, to the annoyance of the other passengers.

From being a large fish in a small pond, I became a small fish in a large pond. The teaching was excellent, but as many had come from opportunity schools in the city where they had been given a head start, I had some catching up to do. Sport was also a big part of my experience, and I represented the school in high jump at the combined high schools' championships, unsuccessfully. I was also given instruction in a group on how to hurdle by the excellent physics teacher Mr Basser. He would have been happy to know that seven of his students went on to be Fellows of the Royal Society in London. One of those was Sir Robert May, who as president of the Royal Society awarded me my Fellowship in 2004.

**Receiving my Fellowship of the Royal Society from Sir Robert May OM AC, President of the Royal Society, in 2004.**

Sadly, my grandmother, whom I adored, was developing cancer and I had to leave after a year with her. Then, I was fortunate to get a scholarship to attend The Scots College as a boarder, and so continue my education in Sydney.

The Scots College was chosen because my father had Scottish ancestry and had been educated at Scotch College in Melbourne. As a boarder at Scots I felt more part of the school. At first, I was given a place in the corridor in Aspinall House, overseen by a kindly senior, Alan Lambert (father of later principal Dr Ian Lambert). Later a place was found in Royle House.

Being shy and away from home for months at a time, I felt quite lonely, especially at weekends, but I was greatly helped in two ways. I participated in cricket, athletics, rugby union and cadets, and on Sundays I was entertained after church by my Uncle Keith, Aunty Kath and their three girls, Margaret, Judith and Elizabeth. They lived at Coogee, where my uncle had his pharmacy. I would catch a tram to their place for lunch where I felt at home. Then they drove me back to school.

**At the GPS rowing regatta in 1951.
This picture is displayed in the Graeme
Clark Centre for Innovation in the
Sciences at the The Scots College.**

Being slightly built, I was also physically challenged playing rugby union as inside centre in the A teams in my early years. Later, I was chosen to play in the senior Royle House team on the wing with bigger, more skilful boys. One lucky save helped give me some standing as a "tough" guy.

Having developed a good defensive batting technique, I remained as an opening bat in the A cricket teams and finished school in the undefeated third eleven. In those days the question of wearing a helmet when facing the fast bowlers did not arise, but fortunately my reflexes were good enough to avoid calamity.

Academically and spiritually, I was greatly influenced by four outstanding teachers: Rhys Jones in English, Dr L. M. "Hoey" Simmons in Chemistry, Fred Pollock in Maths, and the Rev. Bruce Gentle. From Rhys Jones I learned how to summarise information and ideas down to their essentials. From Dr Simmons I learned how observations, in his case chemical reactions, should confirm theory and equations. From Fred Pollock I learned that mathematics is a system of thought where it is essential to show one's proofs. And through Bruce Gentle, the chaplain, I was challenged to think whether life on this tiny planet might be more than just matter, energy and information.

At the end of my four years at Scots, I was very sorry to be leaving. I had made good friends, had lasting memories, learned to be a team player and leader as a sub-prefect, and to take responsibility as a cadet sergeant. I had been in the kit room to hand out sporting gear, on the light squad to turn out the lights before the evening meal and was finding how to cope in life.

Supporting the school enthusiastically was encouraged, but playing the game fairly mattered more than winning.

## University training in medicine

Before my training in medicine, Dad had bought a slightly larger and more comfortable house up the hill at 3 Menangle Road. It was where I would, on the weekends, dissect a human brain kept on the top shelf of the laundry to help satisfy my curiosity about the organ that really defines who we are.

At 16 years of age, in early 1952, I arrived at the UoS thrilled to be studying medicine. My parents managed to find me a landlady in Coogee where I could board close to the beach. In the evenings I taught myself to breaststroke in a nearby rock pool.

In the medical course, every discipline was fresh and exciting, whether it was botany, chemistry, physics or zoology. At the end of my first year, I was pleased to be selected to spend part of my Christmas holidays competing to do dissections of body parts for the anatomy museum. One of my specimens, the front of

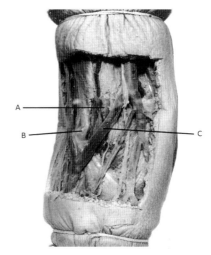

My dissection of the front of the elbow at the end of my first year (1952) is in the anatomy museum at the University of Sydney. A. Brachial artery. B. Tendon of biceps muscle. C. Antecubital vein.

the elbow joint, would help a doctor locate structures that could be damaged when injecting the veins. Many years later, when I was studying electrical stimulation of the forearm to present speech signals to deaf children, my dissection helped me identify the medial cutaneous nerve of the forearm as the site where a stimulus was comfortable. It was the idea behind the "Tickle Talker," which, however, was never needed.

My journey as a Christian with a strong interest in science also commenced at about the same time. I had been advised to join the Student Christian Movement (SCM) and went on a bush retreat camp at Otford on the south coast of NSW. I vividly remember the leader, George

**With my younger brother Bruce on holiday at Avalon, Sydney, in 1954.**

Garnsey, son of Bishop Garnsey, challenging us during our quiet time to invite Jesus Christ into our lives. Partly out of curiosity, I did so and had an amazing experience which is hard to describe in words. I felt the presence of a person accompanied by a fragrant aroma and a sense of peace. It was so real I decided to explore the faith further.

As well as joining the SCM at the university, learning from scientists like Charles Birch, Professor of Zoology and Biology, was a real help in growing spiritually. Charles was a Fellow of the Australian Academy of Science and won the Templeton Prize for relating science and biblical teaching. Charles used to say he would not have become a Christian if it had not been for the evangelicals, whom I assumed to be those who chose a more literal interpretation of the Bible. On the other hand, he would not have continued as a Christian if he had not felt free in the SCM to understand the language of Genesis as popular rather than scientific. My understanding of science and faith are expanded in Chapter 18.

I decided as a medical student to go where the evidence led me in natural and supernatural matters. I could not see the value in theorising about God. If God were real, I would have to test my faith in the world at large. In my term in psychiatry I had to ask whether my initial experience of Christ at the SCM was simply a delusion. Were apparent answers to prayers a happy coincidence? One of the strongest arguments against faith was that in the natural world everything had a cause and effect. So, where was the supernatural domain or being, namely, God? Godless determinism, espoused by the Psychology Department and Professor Anderson in Philosophy, had quite a following.

To better understand the Christian faith, I decided each day to read the Bible more carefully. Without much help, it was difficult to understand passages in the New Testament, and the Old Testament seemed irrelevant. Then I became good friends with Alick Hobbes, a pharmacist working his way through medicine. He had a liberal view of Scripture, and we would often meet for prayer and meditation before classes. I also had other friends who were in the Evangelical Union. I came to respect the sincerity of their faith. One of these friends was Geoff Shead, who was doing very well academically in our course.

After my first year my lodgings had to change, and for the remainder of my medical course I lived with Miss

**My clinical group in fourth-year Medicine, at the Royal Prince Alfred Hospital, Sydney in 1954.**
FRONT ROW (left to right): Alick Hobbes, Agnes Sinclair and Ross Mellick.
BACK ROW (left to right): Ron Summers, Graeme Clark, Tony Chong, Geoff Shead, Henry Pang and Duncan McLaughlin.

Hazel Webber at 58 Grosvenor Street, Summer Hill. She had been a friend of my mother's uncle, Alfred Youdale, our World War I family hero. Her house was near the original Youdale family home in Coniston, at 43 Ormond Street, Ashfield, NSW. I had a small room with just enough space for a bed and wardrobe.

In my third year, physiology attracted me greatly and I enjoyed it so much that I read the textbook on my summer holidays at Avalon, NSW. I also became addicted to swimming. The exercise and cold sharpened the mind. At the end of that year, visual neurophysiologist Professor Peter Bishop suggested I take a year off and do what several others did, a Bachelor of

**Graduation day at the University of Sydney in 1958, with my mother and sister Robin.**

Medical Science degree. At this stage, I was already focussed on studying auditory neurophysiology, but saw advantages in becoming a clinician first and so I declined the offer.

The change in fourth year from pre-clinical work to seeing patients was most welcome to me. We formed ourselves into groups and I was with friends who had diverse interests and skills. They were Geoff Shead, Alick Hobbes (with whom I would come in early on surgical admitting days and learn to diagnose the lumps and bumps before they were removed), Tony Chong (who took me to the horse trots where he bet from his parents' allowance, knowing his days were numbered from polyposis of the colon), Henry Pang (who played table tennis with skill and took me to the genuine Chinese restaurants of Dixon Street) and Ross Mellick (with whom I learned to fence with foil).

At the end of fourth year I was in for a shock. I had tried to learn everything, but when a group of us went to the newspaper printing office to see the results before they came out the next day, I saw my name was not there. I had been given a supplementary exam in microbiology to sit in my summer holidays. A change in study methods was obviously needed.

Memories of clinical training in my fifth and final years include the many lectures from charismatic clinicians such as Sir Thomas Greenaway, who likened the symptoms of thyrotoxicosis to the hearts, diamonds, clubs and spades in a pack of cards. There were the late nights to achieve the 10 deliveries we had to do at the Crown Street Hospital, and at the Children's Hospital I enjoyed being surrounded by children and friendly nurses. Then there was assisting in gynaecological operations, thereby getting close to real surgery.

By the last years of the medical course, learning how to study efficiently had clearly dawned on me. This helped greatly, because in my final year I faced the task of passing 10 written, clinical and oral exams that ultimately could draw on any area in the curriculum. I made sure I had prepared so well that I was able to take five days off before the exams started, just to surf and relax. My mother, however, thought I had had a nervous breakdown and given up. Anyway, after the exams I was not sure I had answered every question correctly and went away so as not to be around when the results came out. At the time, I was on Mount Kosciuszko and when I contacted my mother, she said my friend Ken Perkins had just rung her to say I had topped the year. She, like me, was flabbergasted by the news.

## Hospital residencies and training in anatomy

In 1958, I was appointed as a Junior Resident Medical Officer to the Royal Prince Alfred Hospital (RPAH) in Sydney. I found life tough and exhausting. In the surgery term, it was not unusual to work 40 hours straight without sleep, managing emergencies, assisting at quite major operations, writing patient notes and keeping records. On my weekends off, I would go to our family holiday house in Cronulla and fall asleep in the sun. This was a great way to acquire rodent ulcers. I had to learn to be more efficient in the use of my time and be sure I did not miss a rostered duty, which happened once when I went surfing with Geoff Shead at Manly. This did not go down well with the registrars, though the General Medical Officer Edgar Thompson was surprisingly understanding. This was a highly competitive and hothouse environment for a resident lacking in maturity. At least I had guidance with difficult procedures such as removing an inflamed appendix.

During my internship, I shared a room with Geoff Shead and Bob Beale. We would somehow find time to pray together. Geoff and Bob both went on to become professors in areas of medicine.

At the year's end, when I was not selected by the registrars to be a Senior Resident at RPAH, I felt I was in good company with Earl Owen, later the pioneer in microsurgery, and Russell Vandenburg, later a leading physician. We had to console ourselves as being part of an elite club.

It was a relief to be appointed to the Royal North Shore Hospital, and this turned out for the best. The hospital was nicknamed "the country club" because the pace was less frenetic and there was also a bonding between senior staff and residents, with weekend golf days and formal dinners. At North Shore I had more responsibility, and at night as a Senior Resident Medical Officer I would be on duty for the whole hospital. This was something my father viewed with a mixture of pride and disbelief.

While there I thought I might rethink my goal of becoming an ENT surgeon and be a specialist physician, which in common parlance was becoming a "thinking" doctor rather than a "doing" doctor. But at Royal North Shore Hospital all the interesting medical units had been allocated to those who had previously started their training at that hospital. From a surgical point of view the training was excellent and included being in a specialist thyroid unit with Felix Rundle, Thomas Reeve and Doug Tracey, who were later all distinguished professors of surgery. They demonstrated how good surgery was complemented by excellent clinical research. My term with Ian Monk, a very accomplished cardio-thoracic surgeon, was at a time before coronary bypass surgery and valve replacements but we also experimented with these different surgical procedures on sheep, and thus I learned the ethics of using experimental animals to advance surgical science.

My next goal the following year was to become a qualified surgeon, and I took a position as one of the tutors in anatomy at the UoS in 1960, which enabled me to be fully prepared for the first part of the fellowship exam of the Royal Australasian College of Surgeons. For this exam, we prepared to the extent that someone could throw one of the small bones of the wrist into the air and everyone could identify it before it landed on the ground. I was greatly relieved to pass the exam and have that hurdle over.

Then, to gain more surgical experience, I applied to the RPAH as a surgical registrar, and was delighted to be accepted. The first term was in neurosurgery, which was not a popular option. I had to sleep in the ward when on duty, which was every second night. Once I had to chase a manic patient around the grounds and sedate him with an injection of paraldehyde. But it helped in giving me a good basic knowledge of neurosurgery, and later in knowing how to drill down to the lining of the brain to place the cochlear implant receiver-stimulator package, something an average ear surgeon would have been reluctant to do at the time. For the last two terms I became an ENT registrar and gained a broad range of skills in my now-chosen specialty.

In 1961, it was five years after John Shea Jr from Memphis, Tennessee, carried out the first removal of the stapes bone and its replacement with a Teflon strut to restore middle ear hearing loss due to bone proliferation at its entry to the inner ear. I found the ENT clinic excited about catching up with this new surgery. Barrie Scrivener, a junior surgeon, was practising on human temporal bones, and the head, George Halliday, performed the operations. He would occasionally let us have a peek down the side arm of his operating microscope into what was a new world for me, who was trained in general surgery where most anatomy is on display. In addition, testing of hearing became my responsibility as the registrar, before we had any trained audiologists. I also had to lecture regularly to medical students on a range of general surgical topics to prepare them for their final exams, and I was rostered on for general surgical emergencies. These could be five-day-old appendixes which had to be removed with great care to avoid the dire complications that could occur with any mistakes. I slept in the hospital with Hamilton Bailey's book *Emergency Surgery*, waiting for the next challenge.

## Courtship and marriage

Having been a boarder at The Scots College, an all-boys school, my contact with girls had been minimal. When I had started fourth year of medicine in August 1954, my sister Robin invited two of her MLC friends Margaret Burtenshaw and Alison Turtle home for a weekend. I met them at the Campbelltown railway station and was attracted to Margaret, when she was 15 years of age.

To socialise and show off my sporting prowess, I invited the girls to learn to play golf at the Cobbitty course. My first drive was a momentous hook into the rough, but Margaret seemed impressed. Then teaching her the golf swing by putting my arms around her waist sent tingles through me. A week or two later, I decided to invite her out for a date. This was my first actual date with a girl. I thought of going to the Sydney orchid show and passed on an invitation, via my sister Robin, to Margaret. I was thrilled to be accepted.

Periodically I wrote to Margaret and invited her to Sydney Youth Symphony concerts with fellow fourth-year medical student enthusiasts. I felt a little self-conscious in this group with such a young companion.

**Margaret Burtenshaw,
16 years old, Prefect MLC,
Burwood NSW, 1955.**

In 1955, while I was in fourth year, Margaret was studying for her final school exams in English, French, General Maths, Biology and Geography and finished very well. The next year in the Arts faculty at the UoS she began studying English, History, Music and Psychology, but partway through 1956 she withdrew to help look after her mother who was dying of cancer. In 1957, she started again.

Although I was very fond of Margaret, I wanted to be sure that we would be compatible for marriage, which I believed was a commitment for life, and I periodically went out with other girls. Realising that after my course I would face at least two very demanding years as a resident in hospitals, I wrote to Margaret in October 1957, not long before my finals and said that although I was very fond of her, she should feel free to go out with others.

It was during 1958 when I was a Junior Resident at the RPAH that my contact with Margaret lapsed. She said later that she thought our relationship had finished and was thoroughly absorbed with her studies and the activities of the SCM and its friendship group.

It was not until the end of my term at the Royal North Shore Hospital in 1959 that I realised that it was time to find the right girl and I prayed about it earnestly. It so happened that shortly afterwards I went to visit my sister Robin, who was now flatting in Burwood around the corner from Margaret's home. At the same time Margaret had finished her third-year exams, and thought she would catch up with Robin, who had been studying Pharmacy far away from the Arts faculty. So, there we were face-to-face again, and when I drove her home we couldn't stop talking. We fell into an easy conversation that day, and we soon realised that we were in love.

Our wedding, with Colin and Dorothy Clark, and Olive and Fred Burtenshaw.

In 1960 Margaret was co-president of the SCM and was enrolled to do an Honours year in English. She was working on a thesis on Kenneth McKenzie, the Australian poet and novelist (1913–55), while I was preparing for the first part of a fellowship exam in surgery. We would have many late-night conversations by phone. In April, after her 21st birthday party, we became engaged but kept it a secret till the end of the year. Then in 1961 she taught English and Geography at Frensham boarding school in Mittagong, which was on the train line through Menangle near Camden. We would sometimes meet up on a weekend at Camden, but once I drove up to Mittagong and had a head-on collision in the process, providentially without serious injury. When the school year finished in early December, we had a few weeks to prepare for our marriage, pack and leave for England on 30 December.

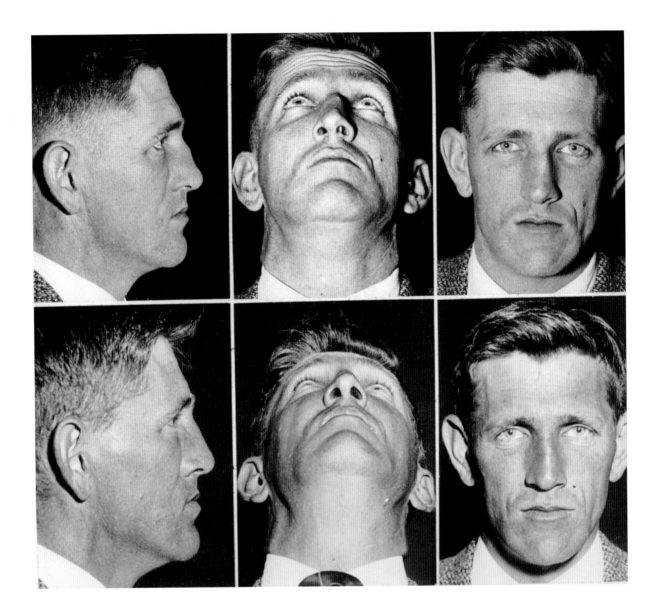

# CHAPTER FOUR

# Becoming an ENT surgeon

In the 1960s, to complete a surgical training it was still necessary to go to the UK, which had a long tradition in developing medicine and surgery. So after marrying, Margaret and I left Sydney on the maiden voyage of the P&O liner *ss Oriana* bound for Southampton, England. This was the usual way to travel to the UK in those days, as it was cheaper than the long two-day plane flight. One ticket still cost about a third of the first year's salary Margaret had just earned.

Our family and friends all lined up opposite the ship, and although we could not hear each other's farewells we maintained a bond with streamers till they snapped. Margaret and I were excited to be starting our new life together, but as we would be away for at least two years it was harder on our parents at such a distance. It was a three-and-a-half-week journey via the Suez Canal, enlivened by meeting up with friends in Perth, a tour of a tea plantation in Sri Lanka, a camel ride in sight of the pyramids in Egypt, and best of all a hair-raising bus ride along the coast from Naples to Salerno. What must it have been like for two of my First Fleet ancestors John Small and Mary Parker when the trip took eight months, and mostly below the deck?

**One of my patients, with nostrils repaired and the deviated nose saddle corrected in the one operation by retaining a cantilever, in Master of Surgery thesis, UoS, 1968.**

This was meant to be our honeymoon, but I brought a small case full of all my surgical notes for the surgical fellowship exams. Margaret was always good-natured about these things and I promised we would have a proper honeymoon after I passed the Edinburgh Fellowship in General Surgery and Pathology.

In London, we acclimatised for the first few days by staying with Margaret's relatives Don and Meg Rose in Uxbridge, where everything looked so beautiful all covered in a light dusting of snow.

## The Edinburgh Fellowship in General Surgery and Pathology

On the weekend, it was off to Edinburgh, which looked so depressing with every building black before the clean air policy was instituted. But we were set to enjoy the historical places—so romantic in these colonials' eyes.

At the Victoria League House, which was set up to look after Commonwealth students, we straightaway settled into the Perthshire room. Margaret found a job as a teacher and I was attending courses at hospitals and the College of Surgeons. I also spent enough time studying in front of our window to become sunburnt. The local pharmacist could not believe it when I came for sunburn cream in February!

Entering the College of Surgeons building I was walking on hallowed ground, where the likes of Sir Joseph Lister had trodden and held forth on antisepsis, the basis for modern surgery. The most impressive lecture was given by an Australian professor Michael Woodruff, whom Mrs Rosalie McCutcheon, resident secretary of the Australian SCM in Sydney, had said we should meet. Had I known all that he had achieved, I would have been in awe. He had graduated with first-class honours in Electronics, and then first-class honours in Medicine at the UoM. After training at the Royal Melbourne Hospital, serving in the armed forces and being imprisoned by the Japanese in Changi, he was appointed as Professor of Surgery at Edinburgh University, where he was the first to pioneer kidney transplants in the UK.

Then in May it was time to prepare to sit the exams for the Fellowship of the Royal Colleges of Surgeons (Edinburgh). As always, I stopped cramming and rested to be sure I could think clearly. Some days later, the college publicly announced the results.

**Margaret in the Perthshire room, Victoria League House, Edinburgh, in early February.**

The successful candidates were to go forward to be congratulated and sign up to pay their dues. I arrived late and found everyone looking for me and so, I immediately deduced that I had made it. I could now be called Mr Clark rather than Dr Clark, and thus became a tiny fragment of the history of the 500-year-old College of Surgeons, the oldest in the world.

## A belated honeymoon

Our belated honeymoon consisted of touring Scotland and Ireland in our Austin van, which also served as our accommodation. To economise, Margaret's relative Don Rose in London, who was an agent for Aladdin heaters, had given us a heater that would double as a primus to cook with. It would be extinguished in the slightest breeze and so we had lots of cold tinned food. The highlights of the trip were seeing Aberdeen, where the Clark ancestors had lived, the north west of Scotland and Skye, as well as the picturesque Irish landscape including the Ring or Kerry, the Stone Age beehives, and the remote Blasket Islands.

The Edinburgh College
of Surgeons in 1962.

## The English Fellowship in ENT Surgery

On arriving back in England, I needed to expand my training and obtain the English Fellowship in ENT Surgery. Hospital appointments were made after an interview to assess personal qualities, not arranged from Australia. Fortunately, the application and interview were satisfactory. I was appointed as a Senior House Officer at the Royal National Throat, Nose and Ear Hospital

**Bristol Royal Infirmary in 1963 where I was senior registrar in otolaryngology and tutor at the University of Bristol.**

(RNTNEH), at Gray's Inn Road in London.

Suitable accommodation was difficult to arrange, but we were accepted to board downstairs in the Hingstons' home in North Finchley. Their house was not completely weather-proof, and the winter turned out to be the coldest for 80 years. Even the North Sea froze, as did the Thames, allowing some people to skate to work. The smog was also so thick that once I followed someone into their drive, and another time found myself driving along the foot-path in Baker Street. The smog crept through cracks in the wall, and a dump of snow around our house was so deep an elderly lady once became partially submerged before we could extract her.

As a Senior House Officer at the RNTNEH, I was seconded to Mr Sam Beard at the associated Golden Square Hospital, founded in 1863 by the pioneering laryngeal surgeon Morel McKenzie.

It was good to form friendships with British trainees, some of whom distinguished themselves later. They included Garfield Davies, John Rice, Keith Ferris and Tony Bull. While in London, I gained experience in drilling out the mastoid bone to cure the mastoid infections which were common there, but rarely seen in Australia. I vividly remember, when operating on my first patient, rocking the stapes bone to make it mobile, and the patient could hear again! At the end of my term in 1962, when a neurosurgeon was snow-bound in the south of England, I was pleased to be able to drain a cerebral abscess in a patient who had become unconscious.

Then, in 1963 I was appointed as a Senior Registrar at the Bristol Royal Infirmary and part-time tutor in Otolaryngology at Bristol University. At this stage, I had to rely heavily on my knowledge and surgical courage. There was much to do. In fact, it was nearly as busy a job as my junior residency at the RPAH in Sydney, but with much more responsibility. In outpatients, there were 40 people to see in a morning session, and that meant approximately five minutes per patient. To manage, my first thought as they came into the cubicle was how to get them out as politely as possible.

Before taking the Bristol position, I let them know I was enrolled in a postgraduate course in cosmetic nasal surgery in Leiden in July 1963. Nasal cosmetic surgery was an area that had been the province of the plastic surgeon, but to correct breathing difficulties at the same time as preventing the nose collapsing, seemed to me to require an ENT surgeon skilled in both areas. The course enabled me to develop my expertise in both aspects of nose surgery.

In Australia we prided ourselves on our general training, which I assumed was so that we could go to the country and deliver babies and handle other emergencies. The American surgeons, on the other

Participating in the nasal surgery course at Leiden University in 1963. Professor van Dishoeck, from Leiden University, and Dr Leland House, from Loma Linda University, are on the right.

hand, were very competent and meticulous about more specialised areas, such as the details of the nasal surgery, and I found this a helpful learning experience. I was pleased to be asked to present a case to the audience.

Before returning to Australia, I had to sit the English Fellowship in ENT Surgery. Margaret was pregnant with our first child and booked to go ahead of me during the middle three months of the pregnancy when complications were most unlikely. I also booked to travel back as a ship's surgeon with the Shaw Saville line to save money, and also to enable me time to sit the Irish Fellowship in ENT in case I failed in London. I resigned my position in Bristol to give me time to prepare for the Fellowship of the Royal Colleges of Surgeons exam. In the meantime, Margaret and I were accommodated by her brother and sister-in-law in their house in New Addington,

**Our Austin van outside
the Hingstons' home in
North Finchley, London.**

London. Leonard was in England to study at the Royal School of Church Music. I studied where best I could find peace and quiet, often in the back-yard which adjoined a wheat field.

Come the exam, I found the written paper straightforward, but I was not so sure about the clinical. I then had to wait for some days to know the result. If you received a thick envelope with all the papers to sign you had passed, but if it was thin you had failed. I opened my thick envelope with great relief!

## Ship's surgeon and fears of appendicitis

The time for Margaret's departure on the maiden voyage of the *Canberra* came all too quickly, and I felt the separation greatly. After she left, I took the opportunity to make a quick visit to some of the famous centres in Europe. Then, alone, I boarded the ship at Tilbury in the London docks and sailed down the Thames on the long trip back home. Entering the Bay of Biscay, I developed what I believed were the signs and symptoms of appendicitis. I knew this could be fatal and faced the possibility of operating on myself with only the bosun to assist. I notified the captain, but said my condition was improving. Regardless, he ordered me off at the next port which was Suez.

After leaving the ship, I remember going ashore watched by a line of seemingly unfriendly foreign faces and I felt very alone. I had been directed to a small Catholic hospital in the back streets of Port Said and there was a warm friendliness about that place. The kindness of the junior doctor meant more to me than the tablet he gave me to sleep. But the sudden transition from being the doctor-in-charge was a shock. An Egyptian surgeon said he would operate on me the next morning. Then I would stay in the hospital till the next ship went by in two months' time! Up to this time I was the self-reliant surgeon, but now events were out of my control. I felt the need to ask someone to pray with me, and a French nun took me to the chapel where we prayed, she in French and I in English. Then things opened up. I discharged myself and got a free lift back to Cairo with a Norwegian returning home after having a broken leg fixed. I arrived in Cairo on Sunday night, having been told by the

**Mealtime on the voyage of the ss *Willem Ruys* in January 1964.**

radio operator on the ship that if I was in trouble I should go to the British embassy. I went, but it was closed. So, I headed for the Hilton hotel where we had called on the way over and asked if they knew how I might find the Australian consul. They said, "That's funny. He has just rung in and is at a party. We can put you through to him." This gentleman told me how to cash my travellers' cheques illegally, though Colonel Nasser had decreed that anyone who did that would go to prison.

I was only able to purchase a flight on a United Arab Airlines Comet back to London. In those days a flight to Australia took two days, and as I was still not sure if I had appendicitis, that was too long a period of uncertainty. So early the next morning, as the mist lifted and while many boarded a Qantas flight to Australia, with only a handful of people, I went to the tarmac for a United Arab Airlines flight to London.

I arrived safely back in London and made contact with my friend Geoff Shead, now Reader in Surgery at London University. He confirmed that I probably did not have appendicitis but that it had resolved. He and his wife kindly let me stay with them and join in their morning prayers

**Dr Bill Hawes, missionary to Borneo with two colleagues in Columbo.**

till I got my passage home on the Dutch ship *Willem Ruys*.

Travelling back without Margaret was a lonely experience. I shared meals with a group of strangers and a cabin with someone who came in drunk every night.

Fortunately, I soon found myself having daily contact with a missionary doctor Bill Hawes, who was going to Borneo.

These events developed my prayer life, which helped me face all the hostility and problems later on in setting out to restore speech understanding for people with a severe/profound sensori-neural hearing loss.

## Specialist practice in Melbourne

Back in Melbourne, Margaret and I were overjoyed to be reunited, and thankful for the accommodation in Malvern Road, East Malvern, found for us by Doreen King, a friend of my father's.

Our obstetrician John Gabriel had his rooms in Albert Street, East Melbourne, which happened to be at the location that nearly 20 years later would become the Bionic Ear Institute (BEI). John Gabriel said that when Margaret was due, he would be on leave, and a locum would manage the delivery. Having had quite a lot of obstetric experience, I thought I might have to help out, but the locum arrived at the very last minute. Our daughter was born on 29 March 1964 at Epworth Hospital, and we named her Sonya Dorothy after my mother.

On my return I entered into a partnership with a medical friend of my father's. He was in fact the reason for my coming to Melbourne, which was made all the more attractive by an appointment as assistant surgeon at the Royal Victorian Eye and Ear Hospital (RVEEH). The partnership offered some financial security. In those days when all positions at public hospitals were honorary, an income depended on referrals from general practitioners, with whom I had no contacts in Melbourne. A disadvantage was that I would only receive a third of the income, but do virtually all the surgery, and thus buy into the practice.

While spending about one-and-a-half days a week earning half the income for the practice, to gain experience and professional acceptance I did honorary public hospital sessions at the RVEEH, the Alfred Hospital, the Austin Hospital and the Repatriation General Hospital. After two years, I had become a senior surgeon at the Repatriation General Hospital and then head of one of the five otolaryngology clinics at the RVEEH.

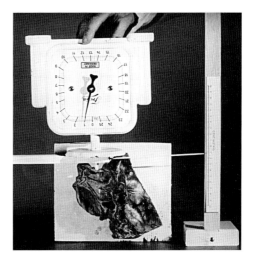

The kitchen balance used for measuring the force applied to the nasal dorsum, showing the collapse when the septal cantilever is not intact.[10]

I was also keen to do some research to study the mechanical effect of cutting through the bones of the nose for cosmetic reasons, at the same time reshaping the supporting strut inside the nose to relieve the breathing difficulty without loss of nasal support. Monash University (MU) Department of Anatomy let me work there and I bought a second-hand kitchen balance for just five dollars to measure the force applied to my dissected noses.[11]

The research showed that it was only necessary to retain a relatively thin antero-superior section of the septum to act as a cantilever to avoid collapse and a saddle nose deformity. I extended this research for a Master of Surgery degree while studying for a PhD degree at the UoS. This helped me in my surgical practice, and I became known as a nasal surgeon, complementing my partner's allergy work. But in finding patients for stapes surgery for deafness, I had trouble competing with the established ear surgeons.

**With Cecily and Sonya on the back steps of 669 Burke Road, East Hawthorn, in 1966.**

After renting for a year in East Malvern, I felt it was time for Margaret and me to buy our own house. It needed to be on a main road to start a new practice in case I wanted to leave the present one. I selected a house for sale at 669 Burke Road, East Hawthorn, that fitted all these needs. But I had to borrow 90% of the purchase price, which would keep me in debt for many years to come. I felt proud to provide what I thought would be a good home for Margaret and family and was surprised that when we first moved our things in, she sat on a suitcase and burst into tears. The house seemed so big and overpowering to her compared to the previous one. The house also required repainting inside and outside, and had other maintenance needs, which helped keep us busy at weekends.

In fact, it proved to be a bonus as it was next to the home of Maurice and Marjorie Belz, who did not have children but kindly took an interest in us. Maurice, Professor of Statistics at the UoM and Marjorie, an anaesthetist, often entertained their friends and colleagues, and at times included us in their gatherings. Later, Maurice was a personal referee for my application for the Chair of Otolaryngology.

Our second daughter Cecily Ann was born at the Jessie McPherson Hospital in Melbourne. Friend John Leeton, who had studied with us in Edinburgh at Victoria League House and now has IVF fame, was the obstetrician.

# PROFESSOR AIDS DEAF

**MELBOURNE, Thurs. — A former Sydney University professor said in Melbourne today that he intended to bring hearing to the stone deaf—those who cannot be helped by hearing aids or surgery.**

Melbourne University has just installed Professor Graeme Clark in the Chair of Otolaryngology at the Royal Victorian Eye and Ear Hospital.

He will study the ears, nose and throat.

This is the only Chair in the subject in Australia and South-East Asia, and one of the few in the world.

Professor Clark, 34, said his work at Sydney University in the last three years indicated that it would be possible to teach totally deaf children to hear and talk like others.

This would be a medical advance as exciting as heart transplants, he said.

Professor Clark said the most important of his studies on the ear was planting electrodes into the inner ear of animals which transformed sounds into waves that could be identified by the brain.

He said he thought that with spacecraft techniques of miniaturisation, deaf people could be fitted with receivers that would stimulate their brain as if they "heard" what was broadcast to them.

Professor Clark said he had also used oscilloscopes — like a miniature TV connected to a microphone — so that deaf children could "see" what they were saying even though they could not hear their own voices.

Another technique Dr. Clark will study is strapping electrical equipment to the arms—again linked to a microphone — so the patient can "feel" differences in voice and intonation.

# CHAPTER FIVE

# The limits for single-channel electrical stimulation of the brain

Although I found all the surgery I was doing satisfying, I believed in 1966 it was time to do research in auditory neurophysiology. I could have commenced in visual neurophysiology as a medical student with Professor Peter Bishop for a Bachelor of Medical Science degree. But there were two drawbacks: it would have been hard to come back to training as a clinician after becoming established in research and, furthermore, I would have been studying visual rather than auditory neurophysiology. I realised basic research and clinical knowledge were both necessary for the development of electrical stimulation of the auditory brain for the restoration of hearing and speech. It would be a multidisciplinary exercise, and for success there needed to be one leader, able to make a range of clinical decisions as well as basic research ones.

The idea of giving the conscious experience of speech to deaf people through electrical stimulation of the auditory pathways was initially derived from the work of Wilder Penfield, who showed that electrical stimulation of the cerebral cortex could induce conscious experiences. In addition, Charles Sherrington, Bernard Katz, John Eccles and others had discovered that neural responses were initiated and propagated by the passage of electrical current. My hope was that simple sounds like tones, and complex sounds such as speech could be coded this way.

**A press report on my plans for the Department of Otolaryngology. My supervisor and friend, Colin Dunlop, underlined words that he disagreed with.**

## Inspired to leave surgical practice for training in auditory neurophysiology

In 1966, during a break between operations, I read an article by US surgeon Blair Simmons about the effects of electrical stimulation of the auditory nerve on one of his deaf patients.[12] This fanned the fire in my belly to do innovative research. Blair's was the first thorough scientific study I had read, but he could not achieve speech understanding. His paper even ended on a negative note about the future of electrical stimulation of the auditory nerve. However, it made me think that if this were possible, it would require many more careful and appropriate scientific studies. The rewards would be so great for deaf people, but it meant committing to the long haul.

**Associate Professor Colin Dunlop at his desk in the small office I shared with him.**

So, the time had come to ask Professor Peter Bishop if I could do research in auditory neurophysiology. I hoped to make a contribution to what was regarded as one of the two last frontiers in medicine (i.e. the restoration of brain function and genetic engineering).

Turning to research meant leaving the specialist practice in Melbourne, and a large sacrifice in salary.

I believed that understanding the neurophysiology of coding simple and complex sounds with electrical stimulation of the central auditory pathways would help me code speech. Consequently, I wrote to Nobel Laureate in neurophysiology, Sir John Eccles, who said that at the age of 31 I was too old to undertake this research. Nevertheless, he kindly sent me a copy of his Boyer lectures. I went ahead anyway.

I was very pleased, therefore, when Professor Peter Bishop accepted my request to return to the Physiology Department in the Anderson Stuart building at the UoS and invited me to work with Dr Colin Dunlop (later an associate professor), who had recently arrived back in Australia as our first auditory neurophysiologist. Thus, I started my journey in January 1967.

**With daughters Sonya and Cecily at our flat in Cremorne, Sydney, in 1967.**

We looked forward to returning to our home state and catching up with our families. First, we had to find somewhere to live not too far from the UoS. What we found was a flat in an old house at Cremorne, which meant a short and mostly delightful ferry ride across the Harbour each morning. I then took up the "thinking habit" on ferry rides and at bus stops and found it a very fruitful exercise.

In August 1968 our third daughter arrived, and we named her Roslyn Lucy after Margaret's mother and my grandmother. This meant that our flat was overcrowded and so we spent the last year of my PhD studies in a rented house in Lane Cove. This gave us the space and freedom we needed, and I could still catch a ferry to work.

When I arrived at the Anderson Stuart building at the UoS to do research with Colin Dunlop, he was very welcoming. He had a small but orderly laboratory with enough equipment to do standard auditory neurophysiological studies, but the Nemetron computer he used for the analyses of brain cell responses was very basic, and I had to wait my turn for repairs. As a result, the recording of data often had to be done photographically.

To fund our expenses, Peter Bishop kindly gave me a salaried position for the first year. This involved lecturing and preparing practical classes for medical students. It was here, while demonstrating the electrical stimulation of a frog's sciatic nerve, that I met Dr David Dewhurst from the UoM. This meeting proved to be of great importance, as David later took a keen interest in my research to develop electrical stimulation of the auditory nerve and encouraged his students to join me. In addition, I obtained a salary through setting up biological studies in the National Acoustics Laboratories to support the work of George Kossoff. He wanted to see

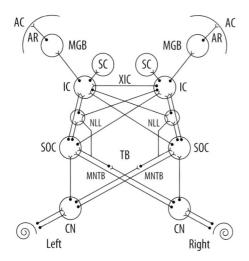

**A diagram of the central auditory brain pathways including the cochlear nucleus (CN), the superior olivary complex (SOC), the inferior colliculus (IC), the medial geniculate body (MGB) and the auditory cortex (AC).**

the biological effects of an ultrasonic probe on the inner ear as a possible cure for Ménière's disease.

Another job I took to meet our expenses was medically examining recruits for the armed forces.

In deciding what questions to research, I had to become very conversant with auditory neurophysiology and electronics, areas that my new associates had spent years studying. As an ENT surgeon, I was very aware of the general structure and function of the ear, but I needed to have a better understanding of how the inner ear functioned. I would also have to know the structure and function of the auditory pathways in the brain, since I would be aiming to stimulate them electrically to emulate the coding of speech sounds.

When it was agreed that I would do research for a PhD rather than an MD degree, I was surprised when Colin Dunlop said that I could study any area of the auditory central nervous system I liked. I had assumed he would decide that for me. After a careful evaluation of the literature, I selected the function of the superior olivary complex, as it had direct implications for the clinical testing of a deaf person's ability to localise sound in space. Being in the brain stem, it was at a lower level in the auditory pathways for coding sound, and it would also be a good centre for later studies on electrical stimulation of the auditory nerve.

However, I did not dare say that my intentions were to achieve electrical stimulation for the relief of a severe/profound sensori-neural deafness. My reluctance was in part due to reports in the literature. The scientific climate made this research difficult. According to Dr Merle Lawrence in 1964: "direct stimulation of the auditory nerve fibres with resultant perception of

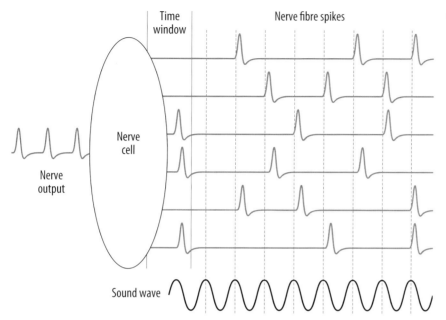

**The action potentials in a group of auditory nerve cells underlying temporal frequency coding.**

(figure labels)
Time window
Nerve fibre spikes
Nerve cell
Nerve output
Sound wave

speech is not feasible."[13] Dr Ed Fowler stated in 1968: "Direct stimulation of the cochlear nerve will from time to time be discovered. There is no indication that it will ever succeed in enabling a patient to readily hear speech."[14]

Still, the auditory nerve was stimulated during neurosurgical operations by Dr Andre Djourno and Dr Charles Eyries in 1957 and 1964.[15] The patients had limited ability to discriminate rate of stimulation but could appreciate a few words. As the auditory nerve was shredded, the results could not be repeated. However, in 1967, at the time I commenced my PhD in auditory neurophysiology, Dr Jerzy Rose and co-workers from Wisconsin, USA reported that a population of auditory nerve fibres fired in time or phase with the sound waves up to a frequency of 5.0 kHz, but a lower limit applied to single fibres. Thus, stimulating speech on a rate basis might have still been possible if a similar temporal pattern of responses could be produced in a group of nerve fibres.[16]

The timing of the intervals between nerve firings (action potentials) is thus important for coding frequency and is normally plotted as a time interval histogram. This tells us how often

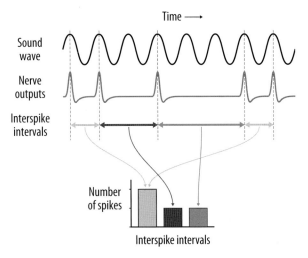

Time ⟶

Sound wave

Nerve outputs

Interspike intervals

Number of spikes

Interspike intervals

**The construction of an interspike interval histogram.**

the nerve fibres fire, the duration of the intervals between the action potentials, and how well they are phase-locked in time to the sine waves.

To see how well sound could be coded with electrical stimulation, I first had to learn how to make electrodes from glass and tungsten wire to record the electrical voltages from single brain cells, and from stainless steel to record those from groups of cells. It was quite exciting to hear the responses coming from single brain cells. An electronic circuit developed as a trigger by Schmitt[17] was set to record the voltage of the cells and feed it to an audio amplifier so we could analyse and hear the cell responses popping away.[18]

The equipment required an infrared diode to prevent electrical artefacts from interfering with my cell recordings, and it cost $100, which I did not have. I went to all hearing aid dealers in Sydney for a $100 donation, and only Stelaid would help. The others said that if my research were successful it would take away their business. Many years later, with its success, the multi-channel cochlear implant supplemented hearing aids, as they could be combined with electrical stimulation in the opposite aided ear and even used in an ear with residual hearing.

Because of my expertise in operating on the pharynx and larynx, I developed an approach to the brainstem through the throat closer to the superior olivary nucleus from which I could more easily record the responses.

Once under way, the experiments to understand more about the neural wiring in the superior olive, and its response to electrical stimulation, were long and tiring. At 4 am one morning, Margaret became so concerned that I had not returned she rang the police. In 1967 there were no mobile phones.

## Studying other areas of auditory physiology

Understanding the physiological mechanisms in a collection of cells in a nucleus of the brain, such as the superior olive, and their response to electrical stimuli, required an intimate knowledge of the neural connections to the cells. Hence, I also worked in the electron microscopic unit to study where the connections occurred, and to understand the nature of the packages of chemicals that caused crosstalk between nerve cells. In one study, I arranged for our technical assistant Jan Harvey to do counting and measurements on my sections so that I would not bias any result. It was quite an original study to relate the shape of the packages (vesicles) to their function, and I published the results in a reputable journal.[19] This experience also taught me about competition in science. A couple

In 1970 I was accused of falsifying my results. Fortunately the analysis had been done by Jan Harvey, the laboratory assistant in Colin Dunlop's laboratory in 1967.

of years later in 1970, after I had gone to the UoM, my supervisor Colin Dunlop invited me back to the UoS to present a seminar to the department, and I included this study. At the conclusion, a senior visual neurophysiologist accused me of falsifying my results. How glad I was that Jan Harvey had done the analysis.

With a strong desire to use my growing physiological expertise to throw light on other clinical issues, I also studied how best to connect artificial prostheses to bones in the middle ear to restore hearing.[20] In 1967, recording electrical activity from the brain through electrodes attached to the scalp was another idea that came to mind. This became a means of assessing auditory brain function, but at the time in physiological circles there was scepticism that the small voltages inside the brain could be recorded from the scalp, as they would be attenuated by the resistance of the bone. However, I discovered that in the experimental animal, voltages from the brainstem could be recorded outside the bone even without the need for summing the electrical recordings.[21] Later, in Melbourne, I was able to extend this research with PhD student Field Rickards to analyse the responses from amplitude-modulated sounds to diagnose a hearing loss in the low frequencies, which had not previously been achieved.[22]

But my main aim in undertaking a PhD degree was to get a solid grounding in neurophysiology to help me determine, in the experimental animal, whether the range of frequencies for good speech understanding could be adequately coded by single-channel electrical stimulation or whether it would require place

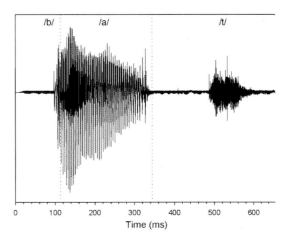

**The patterns of sound for the word "bat." This image shows the demarcated consonant/vowel/ consonant in the word to be coded by electrical stimulation.**

coding with multi-channel stimulation. Single-channel stimulation was being used at the time, but the results were unsatisfactory. I believed far more information would be needed for understanding speech and much later we were able to show multi-channel stimulation worked. But multi-channel stimulation would require a greater emphasis on the place coding of frequency. The complexity of speech is illustrated in the raw waveform for a vowel in the word "bat."

## My opportunity to see if single-channel electrical stimulation would work

At the beginning of 1969, my opportunity to do research on how best to stimulate the brain electrically for speech understanding came when my supervisor Colin Dunlop took study leave and appointed me in charge of his laboratory. I could now do as I wanted. So I undertook research using different rates of electrical stimulation of the auditory brain to help determine to what extent temporal coding could achieve speech understanding for severely/profoundly deaf people. In my first press interview on my appointment to the Chair of Otolaryngology in 1970, I said that this would be a medical advance as exciting as heart transplants. Colin had negative views about the outcomes of research in this area and did not share my enthusiasm.

The first key questions were: Are the auditory nerve fibres in the cochlea too complex for temporal coding with electrical stimulation? What are the limits for coding the temporal information in speech using single-channel stimulation? Will any peripheral nerve degeneration from damage to the cochlea leave enough nerve fibres to code speech information?

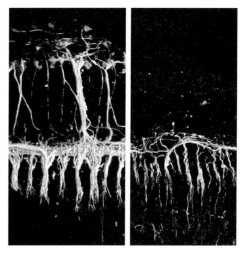

**Cochlear peripheral nerves from the outer and inner hair cell regions in the normal (left) and deafened (right) cochleae.**

My initial neurophysiological research in 1969 on electrical stimulation showed that responses from groups of auditory brain cells and individual cells could not be reproduced at rates greater than 200 pulses per second, which is much less than the 4,000 Hz required for speech perception.[23]

The extent of this reduction in rate of firing suggested that this was not only due to the inherent refractile properties of nerves or brain cells alone, but to inhibitory mechanisms as well. My PhD thesis contained the first reports on experimental physiological studies to compare the responses of cells in the auditory brainstem to sound and electrical stimulation,[24] and to understand how to electrically stimulate the auditory central nervous system. My findings indicated that there was an electro-neural "bottleneck" between sound and the brain, limiting the coding of the timing information.

Thus, I concluded my PhD thesis in 1969 by stating:

Meaningful speech may still be perceived if it can be analysed into its important components and these used for electrical stimulation. More work is required to decide which signals are of greatest importance in speech perception.[25]

I concluded this phase of my research by also predicting that the greatest chance of a successful clinical outcome required the electrodes to be close to the terminal fibres of the auditory nerve for the place coding of frequency.

## Planning the research for multi-channel electrical stimulation of the brain

Multi-channel stimulation was required for the place coding of speech frequencies, and so I would have to:

- determine how to localise current to specific frequency regions in the cochlea;

- find the optimal placement of the electrode array;

- ensure neurobiological safety;

- analyse speech and

- engineer an implantable receiver-stimulator unit.

Having thus reached a crucial point in finding the appropriate electrophysiological treatment of severe deafness, it was disheartening to realise, after completing my PhD degree, that there was nowhere to go to make the next important discoveries for multi-channel stimulation. To follow up my research I would need to find help with a laboratory and support staff. If it had not been for the fact that the UoM had just created the first Chair in Otolaryngology in Australasia and I had a chance of being successful, there would have been no viable possibilities to continue my work. The future, indeed, looked very uncertain.

Nevertheless, I applied for the chair and made my intentions clear. I said, "The surgical treatment of perceptive deafness is where most advances in otological surgery in the next 10 to

**With Margaret celebrating my appointment to the first Chair in Otolaryngology in Australasia.**

20 years are likely to be made." I also said, "One of the main aims would be the restoration of hearing and speech in children who had nerve deafness which was so severe that conventional hearing aids would be ineffective."

When I was contacted in October 1969 and informed that my application to the UoM was successful, I was thrilled and truly thankful for answered prayers that the research would be able to continue. It was the excuse we needed to celebrate at the new revolving restaurant at Centre Point in Sydney.

Then, when the UoM Vice Chancellor Sir David Derham offered me the choice of staying on in Sydney to continue the research until the new department was built or starting in Melbourne, I unhesitatingly said I would return to Melbourne and work in makeshift quarters. I would then be close at hand for the completion of a purpose-built department suited for further electrical stimulation research.

# CHAPTER SIX

# Professor of Otolaryngology and preparing for multi-channel stimulation

When I was appointed as the Professor of Otolaryngology at the UoM, the aim of my initial research was to be sure the results from the neural responses from electrical stimulation of the brain recorded during my PhD were consistent with those for animal perception. This would be closer to the results I might expect in treating deaf patients. Furthermore, I wanted to investigate the question: Could one assume that high rates of electrical stimulation on a single electrode would not code the important higher speech frequencies? Or would other parameters, like intensity or pulse shape, allow single-channel stimulation to be effective? It was a key question, as multi-channel stimulation would be much more expensive.

Single-channel stimulation means transmitting the speech information along a single channel, even if multiple electrodes are inserted and only one electrode selected for use. I commenced my research when appointed to the Chair of Otolaryngology at the UoM, with the aim of multi-channel stimulation with multiple electrodes to transmit the essential speech frequencies on a place-coding basis.

**On Minnamurra Beach, NSW, I discovered that a blade of grass that is flexible at the tip and stiffer at the base would pass upwards around the spiral of a turban shell.**

To design a purpose-built department that would enable us to do the required studies, I had help from John Andersen, a Danish architect and friend, who taught me how to relate design to function. I was keen to make the department visually exciting and had black stripes across the corridor, bright yellow doors and orange carpet. Local Eltham artist Marcus Skipper created a metal wall hanging from offcuts symbolising the ear, technology and the wonderful effect received.

At 34, I was the head of a university department planning research most said would not work, and so I encountered much resistance and hurtful criticism. Having vowed to live in the workplace with prayer and as Jesus had directed, I gained much peace from his teachings and marked verse 12 of chapter 15 in St John's Gospel: "This is my commandment, that ye love one another, as I have loved you."

## Confirming the limitation of single-channel stimulation with behavioural studies in the experimental animal

My research from 1971 to 1976 confirmed the limitation of single-channel stimulation with behavioural studies in the experimental animal. I could not rely on the electrical responses from the brain to give me the final answer but had to see if the limitation occurred perceptually in behaviourally-conditioned experimental animals. Clearly, multi-channel electrical stimulation of the auditory brain for speech understanding was a make-or-break challenge and a once-in-a-lifetime opportunity. Multi-channel stimulation means filtering different speech frequencies and selecting multiple electrodes inserted around the cochlea to transmit information for that frequency on a place-coding basis.

But funds had to be found for the next stage of the research. With only a secretary, a technical officer, an assistant professor and $5,000 for consumables, I would have to be resourceful. At the UoS, Professor Peter Bishop had been very successful in recruiting medical students to take a year off and do research for a Bachelor of Medical Science degree on a small allowance. The UoM had recently commenced a similar program, and when I advertised this during one of my lectures in Anatomy to second-year medical students in 1970, I attracted two students for 1971. We made a conditioning box and used the hospital mortuary as a lab for the first part of the year. It also meant switching from neurophysiology, my first love, and becoming conversant with behavioural conditioning of animals, a whole new field.

With the help of the first student John Nathar and science graduate Howard Kranz in 1971, and with the help of Harry Minas in 1972, we showed that the animals had limited ability to discriminate changes in the rate of stimulation required for speech.[26] The animals' ability to detect differences in rate of stimulation only approximated that for sound at the low frequencies of 100 and 200 Hz, but not at higher rates. This showed there was an electro-neural "bottle-neck" for sounds crucial for the perception of speech. This meant that research should aim at multi-channel stimulation.

The research work is described in John Nathar's thesis:

> As is usual with any form of investigation, there were many people instrumental
> in making this study possible. Foremost to be mentioned in this note of gratitude
> would be my supervisor, Professor G. M. Clark. He was always keenly and actively
> involved in the experiments, offering inspiration, invaluable advice and many
> constructive criticisms. He instilled the spirit, "There is always a solution, if one
> searches hard enough, even until midnight or the next morning." And true enough,
> there were many nights when the experiments were still in progress!

Another important finding was that the experimental animal could discriminate low rates of stimulation from both the low frequency apical and high frequency basal areas of the cochlea. This suggested that place and temporal coding were being processed along separate channels in the brain. Later, in developing a speech code for electrical stimulation, we used this principle to code mid-to-high frequency consonant information as place of stimulation, and low frequency voicing as rate of stimulation across all the electrodes.[27]

These findings helped show that the brain has two main channels for coding frequency information—a spatial and a temporal one. Furthermore, the temporal channel can convey coarse temporal and fine temporo-spatial information.

But I was still not sure whether the frequency information was a specific or a non-specific sensation. In the latter case, the animal would only have been required to distinguish same or different sensations. For that reason, I initiated research with doctoral student Aileen Williams with co-supervision from Professor Gordon Stanley from the Department of Psychology, to see whether the experimental animal could compare complex stimuli according to whether they had a higher or lower pitch. The results suggested that a pitch sensation was produced in the experimental animal by electrically stimulating auditory nerve fibres on a rate basis, either from the basal (high frequency) or apical (low frequency) turns of the cochlea.[28]

These findings supported the development of a speech code in which the mid-to-high formant frequencies of vowels and consonants stimulated different sites along the cochlea, at a rate proportional to the lower voicing frequency.

In a follow-up study with Annette Steel and Ray Black, I found no significant differences for the discrimination of changes in rates and amplitudes of stimulation for different populations of auditory nerve cells over the range 8% to 44%.[29] These were encouraging findings, that people with various degrees of auditory nerve cell loss from the different causes of deafness could receive both temporally and spatially coded frequencies.

## Preparing to do multi-channel electrical stimulation of humans

The experimental findings did not fully predict how to code the overall speech signal, which consists of rapidly varying sound frequencies represented by complex spatio-temporal patterns of sounds. So, I then had to do speech research on human subjects, as we are the only species with well-developed speech and language. This needed a series of studies, supported by biological safety and biomedical engineering research.

A key finding had been that the socket used to connect wires to the cochlea was often accompanied by infection where it passed through the skin. This was the same as the infection rate I had seen the visual neurophysiologists get at the UoS from 1967 to 1969. My surgical judgement was that I should not risk infection with our cochlear implants, though it was a hard and expensive decision to commit the whole program to developing a multi-channel implant where power and data were transmitted through the intact skin. It was good that David Dewhurst, with whom I was now in regular contact, agreed.

## Deciding where to place electrodes
## for multi-channel stimulation

As multi-channel stimulation would require place coding of frequency, in 1974 and 1975 I undertook research on the experimental animal with Ray Black to see where best to place electrodes to localise electrical current to different groups of auditory nerve fibres. We found that with bipolar stimulation (between neighbouring electrodes) and monopolar stimulation

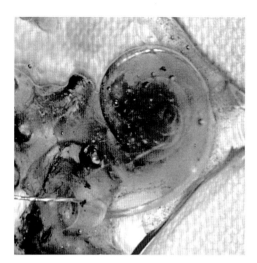

An epoxy resin model of the human cochlea with a Teflon-coated electrode inserted through the round window.[31]

(between an electrode and a distant ground) current was best localised with an electrode in the scala tympani (the lower fluid compartment of the inner ear) rather than in the other two compartments. This was better than stimulating between the upper and lower compartments (scala tympani and vestibuli).[30]

The important frequencies for vowels and consonants lie around the basal turn of the cochlea from approximately 8 mm (8 kHz) to 20 mm (500 Hz), according to the Koenig and Schuknecht scales. The next challenge of inserting electrodes for multi-channel stimulation was to introduce a bundle of electrode wires that would pass this distance without damage to vital structures. I experimented with carriers of medical grade Silastic and Teflon filaments, by inserting them from the round window upwards in acrylic moulds of the cochlea. At first, they would not pass more than 10 mm. This appeared to be due to mechanical properties such as the stiffness of the carrier, and friction against the outer wall. For this reason, I experimented with filaments passed through an opening made in the upper (apical) turn in the cat and human cochleae and found they would pass down into expanding turns all the way to the start of the spiral at the basal turn.[32] But, when I examined the cochleae of the cat under the microscope implanted this way, I found there was significant trauma at the point of insertion.[33] Thus, my challenge was to find a way to pass the electrode upwards through the round window to code mid-to-high frequencies on a place-coding basis.

In 1977, on Minnamurra Beach, NSW, I discovered, with grass blades and sea shells shaped like the cochlea, how the electrode array had to be flexible at the tip and stiffer at the base to pass upwards around the spiral.

This principle was incorporated into our prototype receiver-stimulator electrode bundle and enabled us to meet my schedule on time. It also became the basis for later electrode arrays.

Later, we confirmed this principle mathematically using smaller elements to make up the electrode bundle. The technique is referred to as Finite Element Analysis and was carried out with colleagues in the Department of Mechanical Engineering at MU.[34] Three electrode bundles with different mechanical properties (i.e. uniform stiffness, graded stiffness and a soft tip) were modelled. An electrode bundle with graded stiffness could be inserted with the least trauma.

## Inserting multiple electrodes without damage to vital structures

For the place coding of frequency, we also needed to insert the multi-electrode bundle close to the nerves transmitting the speech frequencies, so that the current could be localised to specific groups of fibres. But in doing this I needed to make sure we did not damage the nerves we planned to stimulate, or they could die back. If an electrode bundle cut through the basilar membrane, there would be a marked loss of nerve or ganglion cells. On the other hand, an electrode bundle could be inserted without loss of the auditory neurons if it did not damage essential structures.

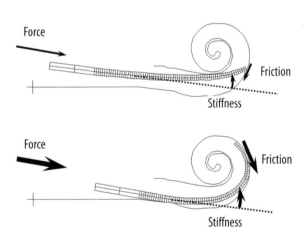

**The forces that would be exerted on electrode carriers inserted into models of the human cochleae.**

Up to this time, it had been considered the cochlea was inviolable and must not be operated on. This view of the ENT fraternity arose due to the loss of hearing that could occur in the case of the disease otosclerosis, when one of the tiny bones in the middle ear was removed where it entered the inner ear and was replaced with a strut. One had to be so careful with this delicate surgery, for any trauma to the underlying membranous inner ear could lead to a total loss of hearing. For that reason, it was being argued, incorrectly, that electrodes inserted into the deafened cochlea could destroy the very auditory nerves they hoped to stimulate. But, the loss of the organ of hearing did not necessarily mean loss of the auditory nerves.

## Preventing damage from electrical stimuli

The electrical stimuli could also damage the nerves. We had to first answer the question of whether it was better to use a constant current or constant voltage stimulator. Electrical current is due to a flow of electrical charge and moving electrons. I favoured developing a constant current stimulator, as I had learned from my earlier neurophysiological studies that it is ultimately the current flowing through the nerve membrane that induces a response, and not the applied voltage per se. Furthermore, fluctuations in tissue resistance could more readily affect the current level with a constant voltage stimulator.[35]

The density of the electric charge and electrode area needed to be optimised. Increasing the width of the bands as far as possible made them safer, but they had to be narrow to ensure a discrete region of the ganglion cell population would be excited. As this could increase the charge density and make them unsafe, a compromise was reached and tested.

To achieve safe charge density levels, there should be no build-up of charge at the interface between the electrode and tissue, otherwise a damaging direct current would be produced. This was avoided by producing biphasic pulses where a positive phase cancelled out the charge from a negative phase.

The maximum stimulus levels to be used in the implant were tested on the experimental animals under adverse conditions, such as 2,000 hours of continuous stimulation. Any damaging effect on the auditory nerve was carefully monitored with neural recordings. The animals' behavioural responses were also measured to ensure they did not experience any distress. After appropriate stimulus durations, the animals were deeply anaesthetised, the temporal bones removed and the cochleae sectioned to study the status of the stimulated ganglion cells. In all cases, the cells appeared healthy and functional.[36] After these studies, I made it a rule that any fundamental change in speech processing strategy or electrode design had to be accompanied by safety studies in the experimental animals.

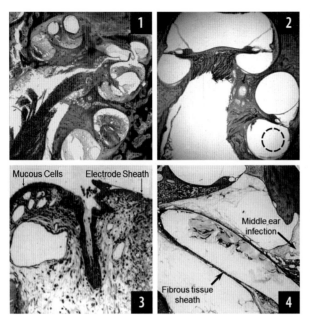

1. Severe damage to the cat cochlea after drilling the overlying bone with superimposed infection. 2. Minimal damage to cat cochlea implanted through the round window. 3. An histological section of the electrode tract showing where the lining fibrous cells attach to the platinum band. It also shows the formation of mucus glands outside, which would combat the introduction of bacteria. 4. An electrode sheath from a fascial graft around the electrode bundle where it enters the inner ear, protecting it from the entry of bacteria.[37]

## Preventing infection entering the inner ear

Prior to implanting our first patient, I knew that a small number of otosclerotic patients who had a stapes bone replaced with a prosthesis had developed a middle ear infection followed by bacterial meningitis and had died. In addition, my histological findings on implanted cochleae in the experimental animals had shown the cochlea could be badly damaged by infection.

We discovered that a fibrous tissue graft around the electrode at its entry point minimised the risk of a middle ear infection being transmitted to the implanted cochlea. This created a tissue sheath with close attachment of the fascial cells to the surface of the metal band, a tissue pathway for the body's lymphoid cells to fight the entering bacteria by the formation of mucus-secreting cells at the electrode entry point to sweep bacteria away.[38]

These studies highlight the importance of using a graft of fascial tissue from the animal's body to seal the entry point of the electrode bundle into the inner ear. For that reason, I recommend the procedure for all surgeries.

# CHAPTER SEVEN

# The need for university training in audiology

In 1970 when I was appointed as the first Chair of ENT Surgery in Australasia, not only was it an opportunity to discover if electrical stimulation of the auditory nerve could give deaf people speech understanding, but it was favourable because deaf people required greater help in managing their loss of hearing. I was approached by Mrs Nancy John and others to join the Advisory Council for Children with Impaired Hearing. They wanted me to play a key role in establishing a training course in audiology and education of the deaf, so that children could be taught to speak and not be dependent on sign languages of the deaf or other alternative modes of communication. They also wanted it under the Faculty of Medicine and within the UoM Department of Otolaryngology (UMDOL). I agreed that audiology was a good fit with otolaryngology and this arrangement was made easier for me by my training in auditory neurophysiology. I could also see the importance of expertise in this discipline for evaluating patients if my research to electrically stimulate the brain were successful. However, I emphasised that education of the deaf should be in the Faculty of Education.

**Undertaking a hearing assessment on Tommy Blair, seven years of age, in the new Department of Otolaryngology on 15 October 1971.**

The parents who rallied around Nancy were a very knowledgeable and formidable group of politically astute people. I learned a lot from them on how to approach governments for funding. They had strong links with the Manchester School of Audiology and Education of the Deaf and were proactive in giving deaf children an auditory-oral education rather than teaching sign language. At the invitation of the Victorian Government, Professor Ian Taylor, Head of the Manchester School, visited Melbourne and made a report to the university and government in favour of a

**The participants in the first School of Audiology in Australia at the University of Melbourne in 1974.**

course. Ian Taylor was also a paediatrician and Professor of Audiology at Manchester University, and Jean Littlejohn was the first female ENT surgeon in Australia. She pioneered the clinical assessment of a hearing loss in infants and young children. This report proved crucial in initiating the courses—the first in Australia.

## Organising the first university training in audiology

There was much to organise and many planning meetings with Nancy John. Our children reflected the frequency of our communications. When playing with toy phones, one was heard to say, "Nancy John speaking." The teaching centre of audiology was best located close to the Royal Victorian Eye and Ear Hospital (RVEEH) and UMDOL. Dr John Lindell, Chairman of the Hospital and Charities Commission, was in favour and helped expedite the plan. I had to plan the course and made it a good mix of basic and clinical sciences. The university wanted it to be at a postgraduate level, so that many undergraduates with diverse backgrounds would not only have job opportunities but could enlarge the scope and status of audiology. To have Audiology within the Faculty of Medicine still required some deft politics.

In preparing to commence the course, as always, I believed in being personally involved and carried out tests myself. One memorable occasion was when the Premier, Sir Henry Bolte, came to see me with a hearing loss. I presented him with the standard word test which included the word "ship." With a high frequency loss, the "p" and "t" sounds are indistinguishable, having the same frequency spectrum. He looked at me with his wry smile. He thought I was testing him on the word "shit."

## Commencing the course in audiology

In 1973, I had to select an academic to lead the UoM course. Previously, audiologists had been graduates in psychology who did in-service training in the Commonwealth Acoustics Laboratories. I was keen on someone with a better knowledge of the physics of sound leading the course, and my PhD student Field Rickards fitted the bill nicely.

In the first year of the course in 1974, a number of experienced audiologists enrolled, putting the pressure on us to achieve a high standard. So, I arranged for Field to complete a Masters course in the discipline with Ian Taylor in Manchester. As chairman of examiners, I had to maintain the course with lectures in the basic sciences, speech and otology while he was away. On Field's return we just managed to keep ahead of the students.

In preparing the first syllabus and brochure,

Field Rickards recording the brain's auditorily-evoked responses through the scalp to see if hearing thresholds could be determined using modulated sound. Located in the University of Melbourne Department of Otolaryngology in 1974.

I conscripted a family "volunteer." Our youngest daughter Merran, at two years old, was just the right age for promoting the course. Fittingly, Merran grew up to become a career audiologist, joined our cochlear implant team and later expanded her interests into paediatric audiology.

## The first audiological research

The courses in audiology, and later speech pathology and education of the deaf, were invaluable in many ways. They enabled our research on recording auditorily-evoked potentials from

**Our youngest daughter Merran on the brochure advertising our first courses in audiology.**

the scalp to be integrated into the training of clinicians. The research with PhD student Field Rickards modulated the amplitudes and frequencies of the auditory stimuli, and showed it was possible to record neural responses from the scalp that resembled the stimuli. With amplitude-modulated stimuli, a Fourier analysis of the scalp recordings made it possible to determine low frequency thresholds. This had not been achieved in young children using behavioural tests. It was important to exclude the presence of low frequency hearing if considering an implant of the cochlea, as this could lead to loss of important residual hearing.

## Showcasing our audiological course

Once the course was well under way, with Field's work on a brainwave audiometer making progress, and my work on electrical stimulation of the brain pathways nearly ready for clinical trial, I decided to showcase our work by running a course with international speakers. I was pleasantly surprised that Jim Jerger, a pioneer in the field, and Ole Bentzen, another established clinician, accepted my invitation. It was a success, except that Ole tripped over an inappropriately placed speaker and broke his arm. The success of the school encouraged me to run a second course and bring Dan Ling and Karl Spens out in 1978. They too were well received.

Dan Ling became a regular visitor and friend to Field and me. When Field and his wife Millie visited us in Eltham, I wanted to impress and brought out my best wine. In the early 1970s, when our young team had presented at the Australian Physiology Society Meeting in Adelaide, we spent part of the time visiting the famous vineyards and came back with some choice vintages, especially from Langhorne Creek. The wine had been left, and so I opened one bottle before the guests arrived and tasted it. To me it was like vinegar. So, I opened a second, and a third bottle, with the same result. When the time came, I went apologetically to serve the wine, but Dan explained it was the wet dog effect. So, we poured off the top layer, and a good night was had disposing of most of our vintage wine.

## Expanding the outreach of the University of Melbourne course in audiology

Field was followed by Barbara Cone-Wesson and then Richard Dowell—who played a key role in the audiological management of implanted patients, especially children, along with his wife Shani Dettman, who was trained as a speech pathologist. Skilled audiologists from the School of Audiology were indeed a benefit for the cochlear implant program. As the audiologists were able in basic sciences as well as clinical studies, they became central to the program. In fact, I believe the advent of the cochlear implant led to a renaissance in audiology, which was losing its relevance due to evoked-response audiometry and middle ear impedance recordings.

The course expanded but there was not enough money allocated by the university for the changes. So, to avoid being thwarted, Brian Pyman and I, with administrative support from Richard Dowell, ran a private practice called Audio Med. We earned enough to cover our costs and with funds left over we created a foundation in 2007 which was given my name. Now, the School of Audiology, Hearing and Speech Science is more independent. It has relocated to the highly regarded Parkville precinct of the UoM and the Graeme Clark Foundation has donated enough to guarantee its continuity.

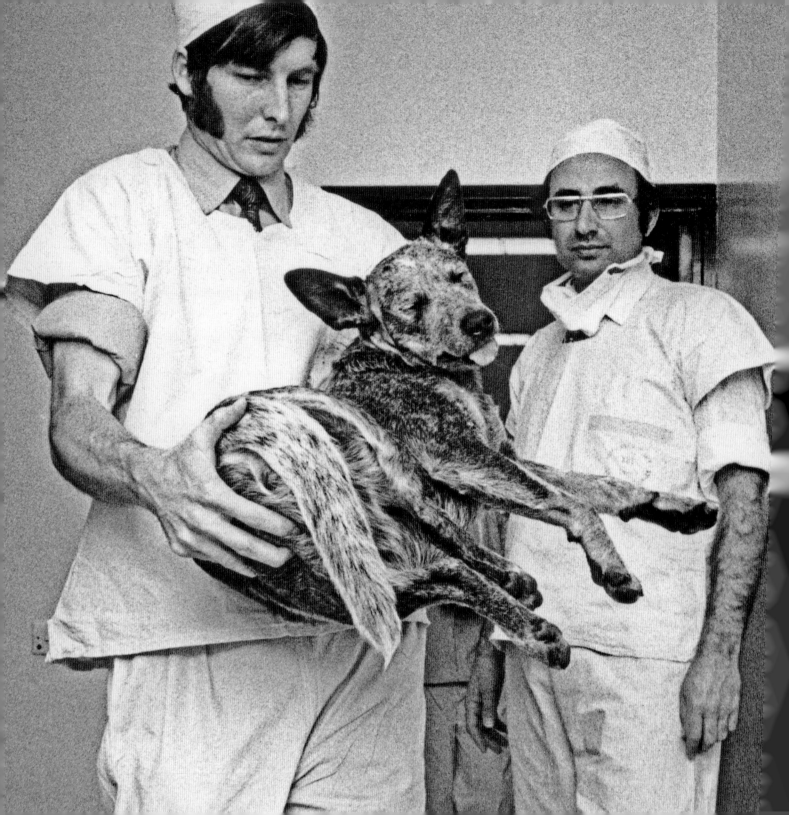

# CHAPTER EIGHT

# Developing the prototype multi-channel cochlear implant

The research on humans to achieve speech understanding required transmission of data and power through intact skin. This would be very expensive, and without money I could do very little. My applications to grant bodies like the National Health and Medical Research Council of Australia (NHMRC) were initially unsuccessful since I was proposing what most overseas and local reviewers considered not feasible, as exemplified in Chapter 5.

## Fundraising

I would have to be well known in the community to attract funds outside the official channels, and I saw contact with the press as an important way of doing this. Fortunately, I developed good relations with the media. One opportunity for a story arose in 1972 when I was approached by a lady who wanted me to see if I could cure her deaf dog. This meant I would need to explore its middle ear for evidence of disease and make electrophysiological recordings from the inner ear to see if it functioned. The idea of an ear surgeon operating on a deaf dog caught the imagination of the press and public, and the whole story finished on the front pages of the evening papers on 5 July 1972, not entirely in my favour.

**A consulting veterinary surgeon carries Cheetah the blue heeler to the operating theatre, watched by Dr David Komesaroff, who designed a special anaesthetic machine for medium-sized animals.**

The story was seen by the Premier of Victoria, Sir Henry Bolte, who was an animal lover. After this publicity he helped me procure funds to complete the outfitting of the university department. Henry invited me to his office to discuss the needs. And, as a good whisky drinker, he

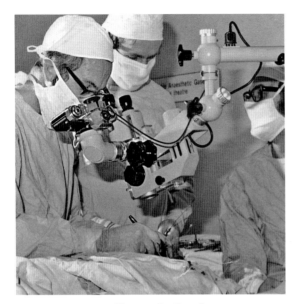

**Operating on Cheetah the dog, assisted by Field Rickards and Don McMahon in the department's experimental theatre.**

offered me a wee drop. I felt there was too much at stake to refuse, but he kept offering more. I only stopped when he assured me the money would come. By this stage I realised I was drunk, and I could barely stagger down the back steps. I sat there at the bottom for at least half an hour hoping no one would come by until I felt sober enough to drive home.

Developing a prototype multi-channel cochlear implant and evaluating speech coding strategies was going to cost some hundreds of thousands of dollars. Nevertheless, I believed if I persisted in receiving small donations from service clubs for after-dinner talks I would at least have $15,000 to purchase a computer with 8 kB of random-access memory (RAM) to start the research. (Smart phones in the 21st century have 2 GB of RAM!) I was not prepared to do experimental surgery on patients without carrying out every study possible to maximise safety and success.

It was very encouraging to find fellowship and support from service clubs at an early stage. Having been associated with the Rotary Club in Camden, I understood their need for after-dinner speakers and got on the circuit in Melbourne. Each time I would receive $200 to $300. I could see it would take a lot of dinners to reach the thousands for my equipment. But then when members of the Apex Club of Melbourne raised $2,000 it was reported on the ABC news, and Sir Reginald Ansett, who was watching, was inspired to run two mini and two major telethons on the television station he owned. These were exciting times, and many gave generously. Children even raided their piggy banks.

Over three years, nearly $250,000 was raised. This included $10,000 from the Lions Club of Melbourne. In 1976, we had reached the stage where the electronics for the implant had been designed and tested on the bench, but they still needed to be reduced in size and incorporated as silicon chips in a hermetically-sealed container. To raise more funds, I needed to show on television the adults and children with deafness and their communication difficulties. However, the Signing Deaf Community did not see it that way, as they considered deafness normal and not in need of sympathy or medical assistance. So, they wrote to Sir Reginald voicing strong criticism of the telethon. Reginald Ansett and the channel did not want to be involved in controversy and decided to downplay the bionic ear as the sole recipient of funds, leaving management to the Deafness Foundation (DF) for

**The Signing Deaf Community demonstrate in Collins Street, Melbourne, against the international multi-channel cochlear implant meeting we ran at the Sofitel Hotel in 1994.**

any further telethons. The dislike of the Signing Deaf Community of cochlear implants was on display years later at an international cochlear implant meeting I held in Melbourne in 1994.

Without the initial funds from the Channel 0 telethons, it would not have been possible to discover how to code speech with electrical stimulation of the brain. For that reason, I thanked Sir Reginald Ansett by installing a commemorative plaque in the UMDOL at the RVEEH. The plaque was created by one of Melbourne's leading sculptors Michael Meszaros OAM and started a gallery of plaques in the department. That first one was unveiled by the finance manager for Channel 0 in the presence of the Honourable Peter Howson and Lady Derham.

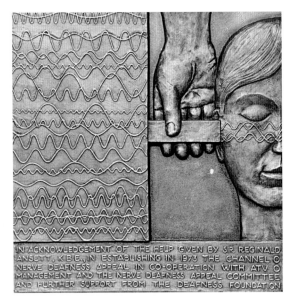

**Channel 0 commemorative plaque
in the University of Melbourne
Department of Otolaryngology
and Royal Victorian Eye and
Ear Hospital in 1979.**

Lions Clubs International (LCI) came to take a special interest in our research, and they helped create the Child Deafness Research Laboratory and Lions Research Fellows. Their support continued for over 20 years. To be guest speaker at different conventions around the state of Victoria was an enjoyable necessity. Sometimes we might sit on bales of hay in a barn in the wheat belt, and at other times be by the sea in the east. I remember impressing the audience once by quoting from a poem by Jonathan Swift titled *His Own Deafness*. As I read "At thunder now no more I start," there was an almighty clap of thunder!

The money raised was put towards a Lions Fellowship which I would like to have kept in perpetuity. That did not happen, but the Lions Fellows did great work and enabled me to appoint talented people when the granting bodies had severe financial constraints. These Lions Fellows included Peter Busby and Pam Dawson, two very able audiologists with the vital role of assessing our implanted children. Another was Peter Blamey, who contributed to improving cochlear implant function. He was followed by David Grayden, who also advanced the coding of speech for cochlear implants. Now he is Head of Neural Engineering as the Clifford Professor at the UoM, with wide-ranging responsibilities for engineers who help people with many and varied disabilities.

Even though we were living in an atmosphere of disbelief and frustration, we ignored it as best we could and made sure we left some time for fun. That included Christmas parties where any or all could perform in our concert after a barbecue in the park.

STANDING (left to right):
John Gwyther, Barbara Weight,
Field Rickards, Ray Black,
Rodney Walkerden, unidentified
technician, Quentin Bailey and
Howard Kranz.
SEATED (left to right):
Rob Shepherd, myself,
Rick Hallworth, Jo Tong,
Joan Maher, Jim Patrick,
Lindsay Cole, Aileen Williams
and Ian Forster.

To further relieve the pressure of leading the research and raising money through the telethons, I found our home and family in Eltham a great place to relax and get back to nature. Periodically we would also go to our holiday house in Kiama for a swim and surf and to see my mother and father in Camden, NSW.

## Engineering the bionic ear

It was a challenge to explore different codes for speech understanding with a system less transparent than a plug and socket. The direct connection of the plug and socket allowed more freedom in the choice of stimuli. But for me the greater risk of infection outweighed the better transparency. I believed that with imagination and creative thinking we could discover the best code, even though we would be limited in the stimulus parameters we could use.

So, we had to draw on my animal neurophysiological findings from 1967 to 1969, behavioural studies in the early 1970s, published data, and the results of my research in speech at the University of Keele in 1976. Not only did the receiver-stimulator have to allow us to find the right stimulus parameters, but it also had to have low power consumption so that we could use small batteries for a wearable speech processor that would sit behind the ear.

Electronic engineering expertise was needed to complete the task. I was led to the right person when I met Dr David Dewhurst on one of his visits from the UoM when I was doing my PhD in neurophysiology at the UoS in 1967. At the time, he was Reader in Biophysics in Physiology, but by 1973 he had become Reader in Bioengineering in the Engineering Department when I discussed the challenges with him. David was very interested and helpful, as he was pioneering the field of biophysics and bioengineering and was motivated by the fact that he had a son who had spina bifida and was paralysed from the waist down. David was developing a computer system he called FRED to assist his son. He then introduced a few very able students from Engineering who were looking for projects that had direct human benefit. The first was Ian Forster, who commenced with us in June 1974 and played the key role in designing our prototype receiver-stimulator for his PhD. Subsequently he was greatly assisted by Jim Patrick. Later, Rod Laird developed a physiologically-based speech processor that we could test for his Master of Engineering degree.

Broadly speaking the questions were:

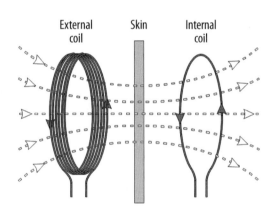

Inductive coupling with external and internal coils for wireless transmission of power and data through intact skin.

## How should we transmit information through the skin to the implant?

We explored the advantages and disadvantages of using electromagnetism, light and ultrasound for the transmission of information and energy, and decided in 1973 and 1974 that the most reliable method was inductive coupling for electromagnetic transmission using an external transmitting coil worn behind the ear and a receiving coil on the surface of the container for the electronics. I recalled that the first demonstration that electricity passing through a coil of wire could produce electricity in another was made by Michael Faraday in August 1831. He was a man of simple faith who had been one of my heroes.

When others started entering the cochlear implant field in the 1970s to discover how to code speech they firstly used plugs and sockets (percutaneous systems) to transmit information to the auditory nerve. But as events turned out we still had the flexibility needed to make the key discovery in 1978.

## Should the implant have its own batteries or receive power from outside?

Power to operate the implant and provide the electricity to stimulate the hearing nerves was obtained from the energy in the radio signals sent through the skin, rather than implanted batteries as with pacemakers, since those would be inconvenient and make the device too large.

## Where should the microphone be placed?

At first, even the site for placing the microphone was unclear, and in 1976 I conceived of it being on the lapel of a jacket. However, during our design phase I came strongly to the view that it had to be close to the ear, because we turn our heads to the direction of the sound that is receiving our attention.

## What should be the design of the electronics to allow us to use a wide range of stimuli to code speech signals?

The receiver-stimulator electronics had to give us the flexibility to choose the right electrical stimuli to represent the speech signals. We used digital rather than analogue circuitry as it was more straightforward to combine the transmitted information for each electrode into a single data stream and recover the information for multi-channel stimulation.

The receiver-stimulator required a decoder/encoder that extracted the controlling signal and power. The controller organised the pattern of stimulation and the backend facilitated the flow of current to the electrodes. The final design for the benchtop model did not have to be completed immediately but could wait for results from our experimental animals and the study I was carrying out with Dr Bill Ainsworth at Keele University in 1976 on the role of formants.

Some details I reported back to the group by audiotapes are now in the Graeme Clark Collection at the National Library of Australia (NLA). The circuit design was achieved through passive (resistors and capacitors) and active (diodes and transistors) components.

The final electronic design outcome was summarised and reported in more detail in the PhD thesis by Ian Forster from the UoM.[39]

## How should the electronics be packaged?

How to package the electronics was a key issue. The body is a very corrosive environment, and salts and proteins can find their way through very fine cracks in materials and cause electronic failure. This is especially likely where the wires leave the package to join the electrode bundle passing to the inner ear. The sealing problem had bedevilled the heart pacemaker industry until Miroslav Kratochvil, an Australian immigrant from Czechoslovakia, discovered that ceramics could be baked to fuse a titanium case with platinum wires, and this idea helped Telectronics (later Nucleus/ Cochlear Ltd) become a leader in the pacemaker industry.[40] It also gave us a great start to the development of the multi-channel cochlear implant. But in discussions with Telectronics, I emphasised that we would need at least 20 wires to exit the package instead of the one or two for a pacemaker. This seemed an unattainable goal to have so many wires bonded to ceramics in such a small space. However, I had always found that if I turned my hand to things, staff would try and go one better. In this case, I got my pottery kiln fired up and with Jim Patrick was ready to see what we could achieve. Then Telectonics was able to appoint gifted Polish engineer Janusz Kuzma, who solved the problem.

**Benchtop receiver-stimulator developed by the University of Melbourne Department of Otolaryngology and Electrical Engineering (1975–1976).**

Did the implant package need a connector in case it failed and another one had to be re-attached to the electrodes in the inner ear?

As we could not know how often the electronics would fail, we had to consider how to replace the implanted receiver-stimulator. Neither were we aware whether it would be detrimental to remove the attached electrode from the inner ear. It seemed advisable then to design a connector that would allow only the package to be changed. However, later I showed this was not necessary as our banded electrode could be easily removed and replaced in the experimental animal. As it turned out, the prototype device Brian Pyman and I implanted failed five years later in 1983 but was easily removed and replaced with the first multi-channel Nucleus/Cohlear Ltd clinical trial device that functioned well till 1998.[41] Professor Rob Briggs removed this implant with some difficulty, leaving 7 of 22 stimulating bands *in situ*, and then successfully inserted the new multi-channel cochlear implant-24 array which functioned well till the patient Rod died in 2007. Post-mortem examination revealed the electrode sheath was very dense around a proximal band of the multi-channel cochlear implant-22 restricting its removal. There were a few causes for this constriction, including prior fracture of the temporal bone, hence the need for new arrays to release anti-inflammatory agents.

## Creating the receiver-stimulator package

In 1976, Ian Forster, with support from Jim Patrick, completed the circuit for the receiver-stimulator with standard off-the-shelf components. They were assembled, connected, and tested on the bench.

Five receiver-stimulator silicon chips connected to a circuit screen printed on a silica wafer in 1977.

**"We implant this behind your left ear and you won't even know it's there."**[42]

The silicon chip, invented in 1961 by Jack Kilby and Robert Noyce, was crucial for the complex circuitry to be made small enough for a receiver-stimulator to be implanted in the body. If older-style transistors had needed to be used, the device would have looked like the one shown in the adjacent cartoon.

In 1976, my vision of a hearing prosthesis as a multi-channel implant was one placed in the mastoid bone behind the ear, with overlying transmitting and receiving coils, and a pocket-sized speech processor with a microphone attached to the lapel.

I was prepared to take time to ensure the design was the best possible even if we lost the race, for a race it had become. The Europeans and Americans were having preliminary meetings to see how best to stimulate the brain.

When the circuit for the benchtop receiver-stimulator was operating correctly, it was ready to be incorporated as a silicon chip. The main company in Australia with the technology for this was AWA Microelectronics, and they considered it too risky. But the Australian telecommunications company, Telecom, was prepared to assist.

Since Australia did not have the expertise we hoped, we could have developed a specially designed circuit on a silicon chip from Silicon Valley in the USA. But it would cost at least $20,000, which I did not have. I made a request to the Australian Government to assist with the funding, writing to all the politicians who had been helpful in the past, but they could not persuade any government body to provide the money. Even with support from friend and former government minister the Honourable Peter Howson, our request was unsuccessful. I felt this was very short-sighted.

142

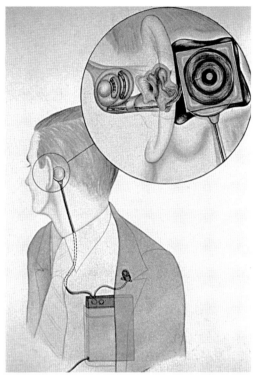

**How I initially conceived the multi-channel cochlear implant in 1976 before it had been fully engineered.**

Then Jim Patrick discovered that the team could achieve a similar outcome with a process referred to as MASTERMOS, where fabricated components were patched together. This would only cost $6,000. I could not afford to lose any staff, but I was able to adjust expenses to achieve this goal. It was not entirely satisfactory, as it took 12 months longer due to all the faults in the process, but I was not prepared to cut corners and so jeopardise patient welfare.

I had to spend time telephoning the USA or arranging meetings in Australia to discuss physiological, biological and surgical design requirements, because Australia did not have a well-developed bioengineering or microelectronics industry.

The next problem to overcome was connecting the 10 silicon chips (two groups of five) into the overall circuits, as the MASTERMOS chips had been designed for each of the stimulus channels, and not as one integrated chip. Shopping around, Jim Patrick found a firm nearby in Melbourne (Hybrid Electronics), run by Wal Berryman. The company could silk-screen print the wires onto a silica substrate the size of a postage stamp.

With this whole development, Australia's expertise was just evolving, with resources that had to be chased up scattered around the continent.

The three silk-screen printed substrates (two for receiver-stimulator electronics and one for receiving and dispensing power) with their silicon chips had to be placed in a container for implantation. The optimal dimensions of the receiver-stimulator package depended on

the anatomy and surgical approach to the inner ear. The standards required for a watertight container were high, as body fluids and enzymes form a hostile environment. A Kovar stainless steel container developed for sending electronics to the moon was used for our cochlear implant. The wires passed through a glass seal, where the glass was melted to bond to the metal of the package and the connecting wires. Even then, fluids and enzymes could permeate along minute pathways or open up cracks in the glass seals through surface tension, and this became one failure mode in two of the three initial UoM patients. The metal lid was soldered to the container, and this created another problem. With time the metals in the solder can migrate and produce corrosion from an electrolytic reaction, and both mechanisms weaken the seal.

**Actual size, a fully assembled implantable University of Melbourne receiver-stimulator (1977–1978).**

In spite of these potential difficulties in using the latest technology, I was not prepared to risk local infection with wires passing through the skin with a plug and socket. For me it was a major surgical decision and an expensive one, but in the long run it set the scene for all future bionic ears and other bionic devices.

During 1977, the stimulus and power circuits were placed in their gold-plated Kovar stainless steel container and connected to the wires passing through a glass seal to a connector at the front, ready to be joined to the electrode wires to be inserted into the cochlea.

Finally, the information to be coded as speech and power was sent through the skin by wireless, and the receiving aerials were placed on the top of the package and connected to the electronics inside.

In 1977, we had thus created the most complex package of electronics for insertion into a patient. Of course, it received a lot of attention from the local and international media. Reports read: "Mini-computer is hope for deaf," from the *Bendigo Advertiser*, 14 July 1977, and "Implant hearing aids to be used in Australia soon," from *The Australian*, 2 September 1977.

I was still puzzled by the question of how to terminate the wires. Some people overseas were attaching them to steel balls, and one group (House Ear) was bringing them out and wrapping them around a Silastic carrier. We decided to try that, but when I had successfully inserted it into a human temporal bone, I paused and thought, "What if we have to take it out?" When I did this, it cut though the central column of the inner ear like a Gigli saw. It would have been a disaster!

The pressure to implant my first patient was now mounting, and the electrode was holding up progress. The surgical group had discussions and Quentin Bailey came up with the suggestion that instead of wrapping wires around the Silastic

The first version of the banded electrode array.

carrier, why not wrap metal bands around it? Even though at first it did not seem to be ideal for localised place coding of frequency, I was amenable to all good suggestions. When the idea was presented at an international meeting in the USA, it was greeted with bemusement as a solution that was too simple. But it had many advantages: it was smoother than metal balls, had lower and safer current densities, and was more tolerant of movement and rotation.

In early 1977, I also had to be sure the multi-electrode bundle would pass far enough around the basal turn of the cochlea to the nerves for speech frequencies, before proceeding with surgery. With that issue weighing heavily on me, I left Eltham for our Christmas holidays in Kiama. The problem had to be solved before I was prepared to operate on the first patient, and I was constantly praying about it, as I had been doing at every stage of our work.

As I related in Chapter 6, we were at Minnamurra Beach when I noticed a turban shell (*Ninella torquata*) that had a similar shape to that of the smaller human cochlea. I was thrilled

146

to find that if the grass blades were flexible at the tip and stiffer at the base, they would pass easily. That was the end of our holiday. We raced back to Melbourne to try out the idea on human temporal bones. And it worked!

# CHAPTER NINE

# Preparing to code speech for electrical stimulation of the brain

Back in 1975, I foresaw that while the construction of the implantable receiver-stimulator was proceeding, I needed to learn more about speech science and what important information to present to a patient on speech understanding, all before a second major telethon was planned in the middle of 1976.

The main work in speech science being done in Australia was by mathematician Terry Caelli. An opportunity arose to explore other possibilities in the UK when I was invited to give a presentation for the British Otolaryngological Society in London held in July 1975. I had also been in touch with Professor Bruce Sayers from Imperial College, London and Professor Adrian Fourcin at University College London. They were happy for me to take study leave with them. Bruce Sayers was focussed on analysing brainwave responses to sensory stimuli, as were Field Rickards and I. Adrian Fourcin had a strong background in speech science and was exploring how to provide single-channel speech understanding with an electrode outside the cochlea. I wanted to use the trip to discuss with them how I could spend my time constructively doing collaborative research in these areas.

**Our family joined a ramble organised by Professor Donald Mackay (top left) at Congleton Edge, Staff, England, in 1976. Donald MacKay showed me that we are responsible and imaginative agents in a universe full of meaning and purpose.**

After a day to recover, on 16 July 1975, I went to Imperial College London. Professor Bruce Sayers was most helpful and said he would be prepared to work with me on a program and provide help. They had a very good setup. I then caught the train from London to Keele University to visit Professor Donald MacKay. I had met

Donald in Melbourne in 1972 when he was the Vice Chancellor's scientific visitor and made contact with him in the hope I would have a chance to study in his centre and engage more thoughtfully with him. He was a most impressive and highly intelligent physicist and neuroscientist. He was also a conservative Christian who argued convincingly for free will and against the philosophy of atheistic determinism. These were issues that I had long wrestled with from my days at the UoS. The MacKays welcomed me to stay in their home and that evening I had a long discussion with him. I wrote to Margaret on Thursday 17 July 1975:

> I am really starting to learn what it means to feed on the Word and how [the Bible] is a living book. This was Donald MacKay's view, and I had a great evening discussing religious matters with him till about midnight. My goodness, he has a clear mind. I get the feeling I am with an intellectual giant. I am also wondering if we should extend our stay next year to enable a few months to be spent at Keele.

The next day, I caught the train to Manchester, where I met Professor Ian Taylor and attended a British audiology conference. I was committed to learning more about this discipline which we had already started in 1974.

Back in London on the Saturday, I went looking for accommodation and schooling for our children during study leave and attended the British ENT Conference, the main reason for my travel with university funding. Then, on Monday 21 July, I gave my paper. It was the first time I had talked about my work on electrical stimulation of the auditory brain to clinicians or scientists overseas. I was listed to give one of 10 workshops at the conference and a presentation of 10 minutes' duration. Only five people turned up. One was Howard House, who said he would let his brother Bill House, who had started single-channel stimulation, know of my work. But I thought at the time it was not much use my making the long and tiring trip for so little exposure. I decided I would not do it again until I had more good data to present. Nevertheless, it was an excellent opportunity to get to know more of my British colleagues, who would in 5 to 10 years' time, as it turned out, become investigators with our cochlear implant.

On the return trip, I found sleep in economy difficult and my mind never far from electrical stimulation of the brain, especially how I was going to insert the electrode bundle. I thought:

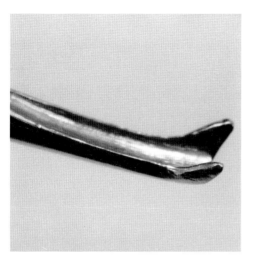

**A micro-claw to facilitate the insertion of the electrode was envisioned during a sleepless night in economy class. It was subsequently manufactured by the emerging company Nucleus/ Cochlear Ltd in 1982.**

"Why not a miniature hand to hold a bundle of electrodes to insert into the inner ear?" That is how the idea of a micro-claw arose.

After returning home, I was startled by the news that the IRA (Irish Republican Army) had bombed the train from Seven Oaks to London! I could do without that spectre. So, I rang Donald MacKay and asked if he had any speech scientists in his centre and if we could come to Keele instead of Seven Oaks. He said that he had Dr Bill Ainsworth working on speech, and they would be very pleased for us to come. Our accommodation was to be arranged through the university and they offered a vacated vicarage, which I gladly accepted. In six months, I would be again on my way to Keele, leaving Field Rickards in charge.

In December, we prepared to travel light to the UK. Packing ourselves, four children and all our luggage into our small Toyota Corolla, we drove the 800 kilometres to spend Christmas in Camden before our trip overseas.

On our arrival in England we travelled by train to Newcastle-under-Lyme. We were met by Graham Jones, the vicar of St George's Anglican Church, and taken to the vicarage. He and his wife had moved to a smaller and warmer house, as they had two children with cystic fibrosis. The huge house had a good central heating system which was costly to run, but would only be used by us for a season. Our girls were fascinated by all the rooms, from cellars to servants' quarters. The vicar still used his office in the front room of the house, because people (not just church members) were used to coming there for help. The Jones family finally lost three children out of four to cystic fibrosis. Years later, in 1997 and aged 60, Graham walked around the coast of England to raise money for medical research. Later, he wrote an inspirational book called *Walking the Edge: A Spirited Trek the Length of the English Coastline*, published by Highland Books in 2001.

On the second night after our arrival, the MacKays invited us to their home to see slides of the area. As a surgeon, I was used to keeping awake even when tired, but to my embarrassment when the lights came on the rest of the family was asleep from jetlag. Later, the MacKay family visited us, and we played games requiring numbers. I could not help feeling that, apart from natural talent, it must have given their children a head start in mathematics. Donald and Valerie MacKay were also most hospitable to us as a family and invited us on rambles in the beautiful countryside. Similarly, Bill and Pam Ainsworth, Ted and Diana Evans, and Pat and Gillian Wilson were all very friendly and we felt part of a large family.

During my research and study program with Bill Ainsworth at the University of Keele, I travelled each day by bus from Newcastle-under-Lyme to Keele University. The main hall, built in 1580, had been in the Sneyd family till it became the university in 1962. It was in beautiful grounds designed by Capability Brown, an advantage for any university to inspire creative thinking. When I turned up for research in speech science in the Department of Communication and Neuroscience, I was given a small room which was on a veranda that extended off a laboratory. Space was very tight, but it had the advantage that the sun's rays streamed in during the morning and I found myself facing the sun as if in worship, as our early ancestors might have done.

## Speech research with Professor Bill Ainsworth at Keele

My research with Bill Ainsworth gave me a fundamental grounding in speech science and in particular about the importance of formants, the acoustic resonances in speech. I was greatly helped by one of Bill's books *Mechanisms of Speech Recognition* in the International Series in Natural Philosophy.[43]

I learned that speech formants use frequencies from resonances due to the changing shapes of the vocal cavities. When a sound frequency is close to the natural frequency of oscillation of a system it vibrates with a relatively large amplitude, referred to as resonance. It is illustrated in organ pipes where the natural frequency of sound in a long organ pipe will have a long wavelength, perceived as a low pitch, and vice-versa for a short organ pipe. In a similar way, the dimensions of the cavities in the oropharynx created by movements of the tongue can produce large oscillations of the speech sounds at different frequencies which are the formants.

At the time, there was strong interest in knowing how the formants contributed to speech comprehension. This was of great importance to telephone engineering, where the system used to compress sound without loss of meaning became known as the vocoder.[44] Further-

**With Bill Ainsworth when I revisited him as a keynote speaker at the Auditory Basis of Speech Perception workshop at the University of Keele in July 1996.**

more, instead of specifying the spectrum of the speech frequencies by the energies in a set of band-pass filters, the frequencies and amplitudes of the formants were extracted and called the "formant vocoder."

With the introduction of digital computers, speech could be represented by pieces of information, rather than a smooth wave, making it much easier to calculate information with the growing popularity of digital computers. This also led to the development of parallel formant synthesisers, which allowed speech information to be transmitted along multiple pathways at once. This new technology was being implemented by Bill Ainsworth with a computer that was quite limited by today's standards. Bill's research projects aimed to improve a parallel formant synthesiser.

I found becoming steeped in speech science a most exciting experience, and as the synthesiser was important for studying speech perception, I commenced a research project on volunteers to learn more about the formant speech cues used by the brain for fricatives (h, f, θ, s, ʃ, v, z). I participated as a subject for Bill in a study in which he was looking at how the brain uses auditory patterns to categorise speech elements. I also engaged with Dr Ted Evans and Dr Pat Wilson to ensure I was up to date with auditory neuroscience as this underlies speech coding. In addition, I needed to find out what was happening in other centres in the UK, Sweden and the USA. All this information would enable me to advise about aspects of the design of the UoM implantable receiver-stimulator. While at Keele I sent audio tapes back to my department to guide the research directions; the tapes are now catalogued in the Graeme Clark Collection in the NLA.

## A visit to Professor Gunnar Fant and the Speech Transmission Research Laboratory in Stockholm

During the time in England, I was keen to visit Gunnar Fant in Stockholm. He had a good reputation in speech research and pioneered the understanding of formants and other important elements in speech. The arrangement was finalised late in the winter when it was still very cold, but I decided to travel by train to see the countryside.

When I arrived, the maximum daytime temperature varied from −6 to −2 degrees Celsius, and on walking around the streets my feet were bitterly cold in my normal shoes. Even the sea was frozen. But I was very impressed with Stockholm—I thought it one of the finest cities I had seen. It was clean, efficient and modern, with some beautiful old buildings. The people were pleasant, and it is always a great help when a reasonable number speak English. On arriving at the Speech Transmission Research Laboratory, I found Gunnar Fant and his group most welcoming. I first engaged in discussion with Gunnar about the wide range of speech studies being done in his laboratories. The results were published in their excellent progress reports, but he stressed that he needed them in recognised scientific journals if he were to receive more funding. His then-deputy Arne Risberg took me around to see all their research and I was impressed.

They had developed a serial formant synthesiser, named the OVE-III processor, for speech recognition, tactile stimulation for deafness and new methods of educating deaf children. Little was said about electrical stimulation of the auditory nerve with a cochlear implant, as they were not convinced from the single-channel studies being done elsewhere that it was a useful method of helping deaf people understand speech.

Primarily, I wanted to learn about their speech recognition programs and computer system as it related to our needs to achieve speech perception with a cochlear implant. There are similarities between how a computer can recognise speech and how to electrically stimulate the brain to restore speech understanding in severely/profoundly deaf people. At the Speech Transmission Laboratories, they had a computer that could operate with just 16,000 bytes of core memory but were getting one

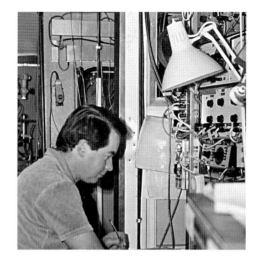

**Ted Evans in his laboratory in 1976.**

that would give them 48,000 bytes of core memory. It still amazes me what could be discovered about speech with the technology at the time—computers that had 16,000 bytes of RAM, compared to today's average computer which has 4 GB of RAM (i.e. a quarter of a million times more capacity).

I talked to Rolf Carlson and Björn Granström about speech perception and was most interested in their serial (one event at a time) formant synthesiser, the OVE-III. When I heard it in action the speech quality was good, and it seemed better than the Holmes parallel formant synthesiser that I had experienced at Keele. They said there were some limitations in its flexibility as a research instrument, but the fricatives were quite good, despite the fact that the "v" sounded like the "w." I thought it would be good to purchase an OVE-III serial synthesiser in addition to getting the parallel synthesiser and I planned to write again to Gunnar Fant for help.

In my tour of their laboratories, I saw interesting work being commenced by Karl Spens, training deaf children to understand speech through tactile stimulation of the fingers. They were also using electronic devices to help children produce more natural speech sounds. I

**Engineer Ian Forster
developing the UoM prototype
cochlear implant in 1976.**

was tested with a series of numbers and got the stimulus patterns correct. Karl had only carried the study out on himself. He needed to evaluate the device on deaf children where months of training would be required in a school situation, without it being hooked up to a computer. He agreed that his program allowed either timing or frequency patterns to be presented, but not both together. Timing information would be useful in re-educating the rhythm of deaf children's speech, but it was more vulnerable to background noise than frequency patterns.

During my visit, I decided I would not catch the train back to London, and so Margaret booked me to fly. It was snowing heavily at the airport, and I turned to a fellow traveller and asked how the planes got down the runway. He politely explained they were all heated, of course.

Meanwhile, Ian Forster was visiting the USA to see what they were doing regarding electrical stimulation. The main points raised were physiological and perceptual. His discussions on perception, like mine with Gunnar Fant, indicated that in designing the implanted receiver-stimulator the fine coding of intensity was not needed, thus leaving more scope for coding frequency or pitch. However, the transmission of the phase of the different speech frequencies travelling along the basilar membrane was being stressed by Michael Merzenich as important for the code. On the other hand, Bill Ainsworth and others in the UK and USA had been studying this and found that at the time it was not of practical importance.

## A visit to John Holmes at the Joint Speech Research Unit in London

As my research was studying the coding of speech by emphasising the formants, I felt it important to visit John Holmes in London, the original designer of the Holmes and Mattingly formant synthesiser. It was a good opportunity to learn what progress he had made in the recognition of speech by recording formants, and how this would help in developing a speech code for electrical stimulation of the auditory brain pathways.

Research in how to recognise speech by analysing the acoustic signal was seen as important for commercial use and in the defence forces, and it was top security. I found this out to my embarrassment in London, when I casually walked into the Joint Speech Research Unit and was abruptly confronted by a guard.

When I met John Holmes, he kindly showed me how, with more computer power than Bill Ainsworth's system, he extracted a greater number of formant frequencies and could recognise speech more accurately. But I could see that this would be too complicated to use for a speech code with our future electrical stimulation of the auditory brain in Melbourne.

## A four-day physiological and biophysical experiment by Ted Evans and Pat Wilson

To determine the most effective coding of speech with electrical stimulation would require flexibility in the design of the receiver-stimulator. I considered it was also better to code speech by providing the basic information (bottom-up) and then facilitating the higher brain centres to make sense of it (top-down). Thus, as the neurophysiology of the auditory nervous system was important for bottom-up processing, I viewed with eagerness the opportunity to assist in a four-day neurophysiological and biophysical experiment on a cat. Ted Evans and Pat Wilson had a shortage of animals and had to be economical in their use. Ted was meticulous with his surgery and Pat was just as expert in psychoacoustics. Important information was obtained that showed the brain cells filtered out different frequencies, supporting multi-channel stimulation.

As outlined in one of the audiotapes in the Graeme Clark Collection at the NLA:

Ted Evans did the appropriate exposure of the basilar membrane for Pat Wilson's capacitive probe study over the next one-and-a-half days. The capacitive probe is extremely small, and it measures fine movements at a very precise location along the basilar membrane. He was able to make a series of phase measurements for different intensities and different locations in the basal turn—from the 40 kHz area down to 8 kHz, making it possible to plot a travelling wave along the membrane. Furthermore, over a 100-dB intensity range, the response from the basilar membrane was linear, but there were some peculiar phase changes seen. This was valuable information for the future coding of sound with electrical stimulation.

## A visit for the 100th anniversary dinner of the British Physiological Society

Having a strong interest in auditory neurophysiology, I took the opportunity in London to attend the 100th anniversary dinner of the British Physiological Society as a member of the Australian Physiological Society. There have been so many British physiologists who have pioneered the field. It was memorable to attend and absorb some of the history. The event was held at the University College, London, which I understand was the founder of the British Physiological Society. The standard of the demonstrations was good and the dinner superb. They also had an interesting exhibit at the official table in which the secretary was presented with a scratching dog. This sculpted scratching dog had great significance, as Sherrington's original scratching dog gave him the inspiration for making his discoveries on the neural reflex using both mechanical and electrical stimuli. (For further details see the audio in the Graeme Clark Collection at the NLA.)

## Meeting Giles Brindley at the Psychiatric Research Institute at Maudley Hospital, London

I was aware of the research of Giles Brindley who was the first to electrically stimulate the visual cortex to restore sight to the blind. Giles kindly agreed to meet me while I was in London. David Dewhurst had been a regular visitor due to his strong interest in neural engineering. I was told they had implanted two prostheses over the visual cortex and were planning to do a third. The first patient had 71 electrodes; 30 worked initially but only five were working at the time of my visit. The second patient was an older person and again, there were 70 electrodes implanted and 35 still working. Electrical stimulation of each electrode produced a spot of light called a phosphene. The phosphenes in the second patient were not so precise as with the first patient and therefore the hope for perception wasn't as good. They were thinking of putting another one back in the first patient because of her ability to perceive clear, distinct phosphenes.

I went primarily to discuss the question of packaging, as this applied to the research I was proposing into multi-electrode stimulation of the auditory pathways. But I was disappointed Giles did not give me a very clear picture of their development. He had been cooking up some of their electronic packages for nine years in salt solution. Periodically they got them out to test them and they still worked. (For further details see the audio in the Graeme Clark Collection at the NLA.)

## Surface preparation histology and equipment for experimental studies

There was much discussion at the Physiology Society meeting and at Keele about the importance of selectively destroying cochlear hair cells to study the effects and treatment of deafness. I considered this would be an important animal model for us to study the effects of electrical stimulation in deaf people and sent information back to prepare for this work. I wrote at the time:

> The first step is to give controlled doses of neomycin, kanamycin and dihydrostreptomycin to cause hair cell loss and then carry out surface preparation histology to see the extent of the loss. If we could control the loss of inner or outer hair cells or auditory nerve fibres, we could determine the effects of electrical stimulation for the different pathologies leading to deafness.

I stated that when I returned, I would like to continue this electro-physiological research in the guinea pig. The details of the equipment needed are outlined in the Graeme Clark Collection at the NLA.

## Surgical equipment needed

As time was moving on until I returned, I also had to focus on ensuring that we would have the best equipment available for the surgery I proposed. This involved investigations in both London and Sweden. To show the range of biomedical and surgical preparations needed, the details have been more fully reported in the Graeme Clark Collection at the NLA.

Firstly, I had discussions with Zeiss London about our immediate needs. I also enquired about very fine micro burrs with an outside diameter of 0.1 mm, 0.2 mm and 0.3 mm to drill into the inner ear. The smallest diamond paste burr that could be made commercially had an outside diameter of 0.6 mm. I then contacted a Swedish firm, who made small burrs with an outside diameter of 0.1 mm, 0.2 mm and 0.3 mm but they said they could not be covered evenly with diamond particles, so I thought this was something we needed to develop ourselves.

## Return to Melbourne to prepare for the forthcoming telethon

As there was a major telethon being held to fund essential areas of our cochlear implant research, I needed to return to oversee the UMDOL's activities, and to ensure in advance that the presentation of our work would be appealing. I arrived home one week before the event. My comments are in the Graeme Clark Collection at the NLA.

When back in Melbourne in May I found time to continue my study to determine how the perception of speech elements (phonemes) is important in the development of language in deaf children. But my prime responsibility was to oversee the completion of the prototype receiver-stimulator for implantation, select suitable patients and make sure we had all the right surgical procedures in place. Furthermore, to pursue my now strong interest in speech coding for cochlear implants, I wrote a letter of introduction to Dr Bruce Millar, who had been a doctoral student with Donald MacKay.

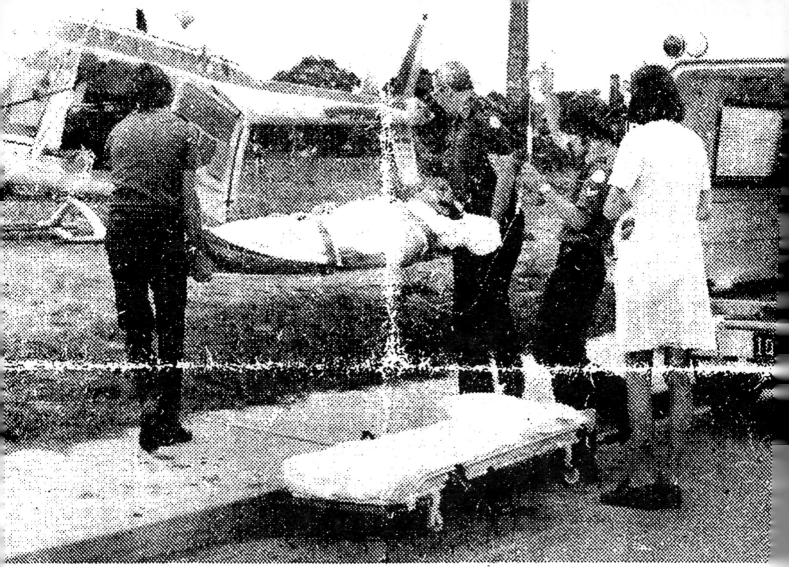

**DANDENONG** man who suffered head injuries when his car le[ft]
[t]he road in freak circumstances was transferred to Melbourne b[y]
[t]he Angel of Mercy helicopter ambulance on Monday morning.

Mr R. Saunders, of Birdwood Ave, was admitted to Dandenong and District Hospital on Saturday afternoon.

His car left the road and struck a pole on the corner

Pde, Dandenong West.

Ambulancemen said t[hey]
believed wood Mr Saun[ders]
was carrying in his
struck something, sw[ung]
around and hit him on [the]
head, causing him to [...]

# CHAPTER TEN

# Preparation for surgery and patient selection

In parallel with fundamental research, and to create the implant package and electrode bundle, there were other vitally important issues:

- developing the surgical procedure on temporal bones to avoid damaging the facial nerve, and providing entry to the inner ear and inserting the electrode to avoid trauma to the inner ear;

- selecting suitable patients;

- funding the clinical work;

- developing a protocol to minimise the risk of infection and

- receiving ethics approval.

## Surgical procedure

**A press report of Rod Saunders being transferred by the *Angel of Mercy* helicopter to a hospital in Melbourne with a head injury.**

In documenting the surgical steps in a manual (one of the originals is in the Graeme Clark Collection in the NLA), I worked with my assistant surgeon Brian Pyman, who had recently gained his qualifications and was the only surgeon excited about the possibilities this work would offer. He was a godsend. I was determined to master the steps of drilling the approach to the inner ear with its variations in the anatomy, but also to decide the type of drill bits to use at various stages of the operation. I gave much thought to the best way to view the round window into the inner ear and how to drill around it, open the window and visualise the channel to be implanted. The right suckers were needed here, and the small hand-like claw to help steer the electrode tip into the inner ear.

Once the biomechanical properties of the electrode bundle, its site of insertion and the design of the stimulating electrode bands had been finalised, we were ready for our clinical research studies. To ensure the implant would produce minimal trauma, it was inserted by experienced surgeons in nine fresh human temporal bones, which were then sectioned, and examined for damage. Minimal histological damage was seen, and primarily in a localised region of the spiral ligament. This would not lead to significant neural degeneration or compromise the efficacy of our multi-channel prosthesis.

## Selection of suitable patients

Two years before the first operation, I had selected four profoundly deaf candidates from our clinic to ensure we had the right assessment protocols in place. These included a medical examination to determine the cause of deafness, an audiological assessment of the level and nature of the hearing loss and special x-rays to see the state of the cochlea. In the end, none of the patients were suitable. But the process had shown that there was no need for the battery of psychological tests being undertaken by some single-channel implant groups to justify minimal improvements.

Still, in 1977, I had no patients. No doctor would refer any, as they did not believe what I was doing was acceptable. But unknown to me, Rod Saunders had a major car accident on 15 January 1977. He was knocked unconscious and made totally deaf. He was airlifted to St Vincent's Hospital for neurosurgery.

Part of his skull bone was removed to clamp the bleeding artery at the base of his brain. After he recovered, he realised he could not hear and had to communicate with his family using notes. For many months he had to adjust to his plight, which is described by his eldest daughter Christine in Chapter 1. As she recalls, one day her mother saw the article in the press which referred to my work to develop a bionic ear. In that article I was reported as saying:

> Nerve deafness is the last frontier in diseases of the ear.
> However, help could be on the way with the computer system
> which will soon be implanted for the first time in a patient.

Reporter Deidre Nolan goes on to say:

> Even if successful, the computer system will not enable perfect hearing.
> It will not pick up high-fidelity sound and there will be some background
> noise. However, patients should be able to hear and understand speech.

That motivated the husband and wife to go looking for me. They started at Jean Littlejohn's Deafness Investigation and Research Unit at the RVEEH.

Fortunately, one of the department's audiologists, Angela Marshall, was seconded to the unit and learned that Rod Saunders, whose story begins this book, wanted to find out how to contact me. Angela's sympathies were with the university and she made the introduction. Shortly afterwards, a second person, George Watson, arrived through the Repatriation Department and he was also a good candidate. He was referred by George Themistoklis, another UoM-trained audiologist.

Both Rod and George were keen to be the first. But I explained that before making that decision I would need another test to see if their hearing nerves functioned. A wire was placed on the surface of the bony cochlea in the middle ear to electrically stimulate the auditory nerve. The test proved positive on both, and Rod heard pitch increases with ascending pulse rates.

I set a date for the first surgery in early 1978 and hoped it would become "implant day." But there were delays on the engineering side and I had to get agreement that an "absolute deadline" would be 1 August 1978. I also had to decide whether to operate on Rod or George first. This was an important decision that could affect the success of the whole program. I selected Rod, as he had been deafened recently and I thought his brain would still be best able to recall his conscious experience of sounds. Furthermore, as he sang in his church choir, he should have a good knowledge of musical scales, of help to us in learning what he experienced with electrical stimuli.

I rang his wife Margaret to tell her the news and to ask if Rod was in agreement. I understand they were anxiously awaiting the decision. Rod was working in the garden, and so Margaret had to use her normal way of communication to get his attention—a direct hit with a clod of dirt. He was delighted to hear the news.

## A search for funding

Early in 1978, I endeavoured to find ways of funding the clinical work before and after Rod's operation scheduled for later in the year. I was approached by Dr Bill Coyne, a representative for 3M. The company was looking to use the cochlear implant to enter the medical instrument market. Some months later, after I had commenced fruitful discussions with the Australian Government, 3M contacted me saying that our system was too complex and they would be working with the House/3M, then with the Vienna/3M single-channel devices.

In June 1978, I did a preliminary market survey on the incidence of a profound hearing loss to satisfy myself that my proposal would benefit a reasonable number of people, as some were saying I had exaggerated the incidence to attract funding. Then, in approaching the Australian Government for help, I went to the top. I wrote to the Prime Minister, the Right Honourable Malcolm Fraser on 20 July 1978, and the letter was passed to the Minister for Productivity, the Honourable Ian Macphee AO.

At that time, the government was looking to encourage collaboration between universities and industry. It was heartening to receive a reply from the Prime Minister on 28 August 1978 that the government had set up funding in the 1978–1979 budget for industrial research. Further details can be found in the Graeme Clark Collection in the NLA. During this review process, I was also able to inform the government of the good and exciting results we had just obtained.

Prime Minister
Canberra
28 August 1978

Dear Professor Clark,

Thank you for your letter of 20 July concerning the artificial hearing device developed by the University of Melbourne for surgical implantation into patients who are profoundly or completely deaf.

Your letter highlights the need to capitalise on Australia's current lead in this field, particularly in the light of planned developments in Europe and North America. In this respect, you will notice that the 1978/79 Budget provides for enhanced Government support for industrial research and development including the provision of support for the undertaking of "public interest" research projects …

Yours sincerely,

Malcolm Fraser

This support from the government was very fortuitous, as outlined in a later email to me on 22 March 2015 by the Honourable Ian Macphee AO, who had been Director of the Chamber of Manufacturers before entering politics. He said:

In 1976, Malcolm Fraser had the foresight to create a Department of Productivity to incorporate human resource management, quality control, innovation, skill enhancement and enterprise bargaining. A vast range of departmental activities were merged to enable Australians to understand the nature of productivity, a word rarely used in Australia then. Unions and employers were engaged, where possible, with scientists and others trying to set an example for cost reduction and increased efficiency and job satisfaction. Research and development was a major part of the interaction. It was during this period that I encountered Graeme Clark, who was inventing the bionic ear. Despite the oil crisis and the inherited deficit, Malcolm, Peter and Doug Anthony persuaded cabinet to fund further research for what became the cochlear ear implant. There were other achievements, but that is one of the most notable. Employees in the department exchanged jobs with some in the private sector so that each sector could understand the role of the other better. That was an initiative with which Malcolm agreed.

Led by the department's secretary Paul Schulz, the government made a careful due diligence study that included meeting my wife Margaret. They considered one's spouse would be important in their success, and they were right. In selecting from tendering companies, David Dewhurst and I were both asked for our opinion on the best background required in this new field, and we considered that safe packaging of the electronics was most important. This was where Telectronics had considerably more experience than other tendering companies, and they could more easily develop the electronics for the speech coding. That would give them a marketing advantage over any other competitors emerging in the field.

The government committee also decided that we at the UoM would need to not only provide essential research input, but also evaluate the device to show that it would work for a wide and varied population. Before the end of the year on 6 December 1978, there was a crucial meeting held in the office of the Vice Principal, Ray Marginson, at the UoM. Paul Trainor, other senior members of Telectronics, David Dewhurst and I had to decide what we at the university would be committed to if the funding proposal was approved. Paul Trainor was still not very confident that he would be backing a winner, and even requested they take out an insurance policy on my life, which I declined. We finally agreed that I would operate on at least two more adults by the end of 1979 to give an indication that our good results were more generally applicable. It was difficult to agree to more, as I was not getting referrals from colleagues, and I was firmly of the view that it was best to carefully examine a small number of patients well. In my surgical career, I had seen a numbers game being played all too often, sometimes with bad results.

## A protocol to minimise the risk of infection

The prevention of infection at the time of surgery was especially important for the cochlear implant operation. Implanting a foreign body can increase the risk of infection spreading to the inner ear with serious consequences and even meningitis. Brian Pyman and I developed a setup in the theatre to allow us to operate in a horizontal flow of sterile air. Special precautions were adopted with gowning and movement of personnel.[45]

## Ethics

In the 1970s, ethics committees were just being created in the major hospitals because the era of clinical research in Australia had only recently arrived. I helped instigate a committee for our cochlear implant research at the RVEEH. It needed independent personnel consisting of a lawyer, a parent of a deaf child, another ENT surgeon and a representative of the hospital, while I acted as a spokesperson for the clinical research team. The hospital contacted their insurers, and I already had medical insurance as a surgeon. In addition, I made sure that Rod was aware of the possible risks. These were similar to those of major ear and temporal bone surgery but with a greater chance of meningitis and wound infection. In addition, we could not be certain in spite of rigorous tests that the device would work. I also explained that we had done all we could to keep these risks low. I would keep him informed about the results and he could withdraw from the study at any time.

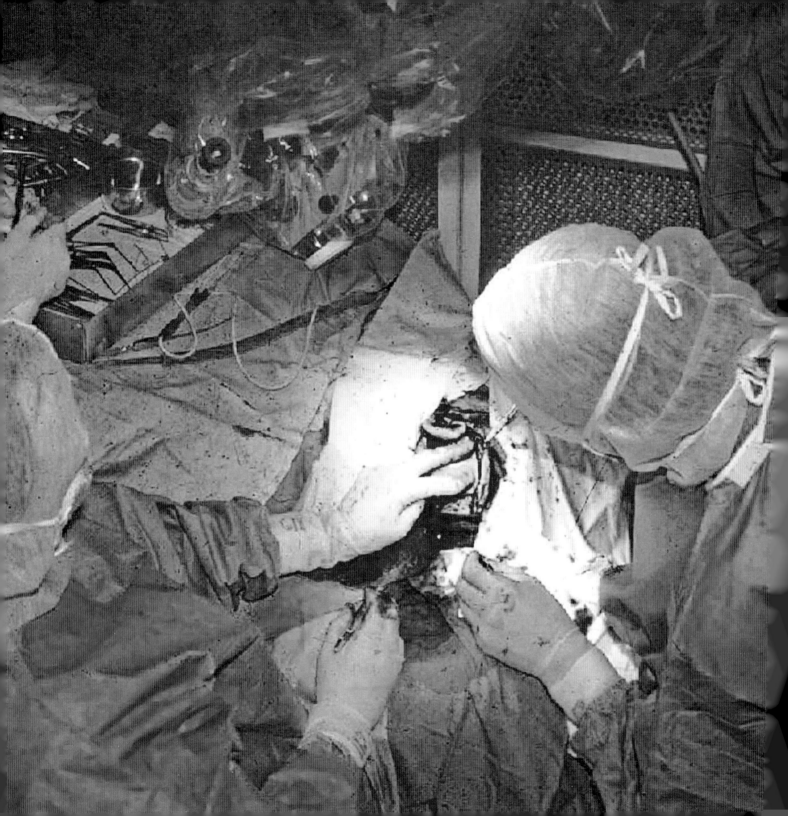

# CHAPTER ELEVEN

# Surgery on the first multi-channel cochlear implant patient

## The operation

As Tuesday 1 August 1978 had been set for the first operation, Margaret and I went away for a weekend of relaxation and prayer at the Blue Dandenongs Motel at Kalorama, out of Melbourne. On arriving back on Monday, I found a flurry of activity as the engineers bustled around doing the last checks on the device. Then, early on Tuesday, I left home and arrived at the operating theatre. There was an air of expectancy around, and certainly in the operating theatre. This is best epitomised by the remark of my ophthalmological colleague and good friend Professor Gerard Crock, who was standing outside my theatre. As I passed, he said, "Professor Clark, your moment of truth has arrived." How right he was.

Before I scrubbed and entered my theatre, I went to see Rod, who was being made ready for the surgery. Although heavily sedated with Valium, he was conscious enough to understand my words of assurance. With plenty of surgical experience behind me, I always felt it important to see my patients before operating on them. I was, after all, taking their lives in my hands.

**Brian Pyman and I performed the cochlear implant operation on Rod Saunders on 1 August 1978.**

I commenced the surgery aware of a conversation I had with a speech pathologist just a few days prior to the operation, when she had whispered to me that a colleague had said that by doing the multi-channel operation, I might kill my patient. But undaunted, I slid the knife blade along the planned pathway to expose the underlying mastoid bone, ably assisted by Associate Professor Brian Pyman and Sister Gill Martin.

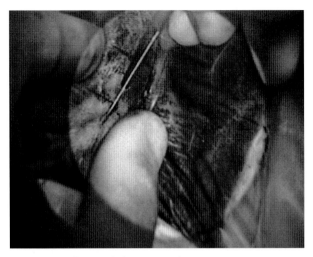

**A screenshot of the initial incision on my first patient to have a multi-channel cochlear implant on 1 August 1978.**

I removed the air cells in the mastoid bone behind the ear with a drill, thinking it best to remove most cells to minimise their being infected, although this lengthened the operation. It also gave me a wide approach to the inner ear from the rear for the electrode insertion.

As this meant skimming over the nerve to the face, I did so with utmost care, using a diamond paste burr, not wanting to cause paralysis of the face as I had done once in Bristol, where I had to use gauges and not a drill, for a mastoid infection. Brian Pyman, who was sharing the surgery, inserted the electrode bundle to the expected 25 mm.

The overall operation went for eight hours, made longer by time taken to make and sterilise a Silastic mould of the mastoid cavity to hold the implant package in place, and avoid the risk of it rocking forward into the space that I had created. Moreover, for the first time I was drilling down to the thick membrane (dura mater) surrounding the brain, something not normally done by ENT surgeons, and I wanted to make sure there would be no bleeding from the surrounding veins. Furthermore, I was operating on the side where a section of his skull bone had been removed to control the bleeding from his head injury and I only just had room to drill the bed for his implant package without entering his cranial cavity.

## Post-operative recovery

As Rod recovered from the anaesthetic, my first thought was to ask him to smile so I could be sure drilling over the nerve to his face had not damaged it. That night, after a couple of calls to the nursing staff to satisfy myself there were no signs of haemorrhage, I slept fitfully.

Rod recovered well from the operation, but some days after the surgery there was a code blue for an emergency on the floor where he was recuperating. I dashed up the steps, with the words "I might kill my patient" resonating in my mind and discovered Rod had collapsed. This caused quite a stir in the ward. However, I soon realised he had only fainted, and had done so when Sister Lyn Hickman was removing the dressing. ENT surgeons get used to young, healthy males fainting when approached with a long needle to wash out their nasal sinuses, so I was very familiar with this happening.

## Celebration

Brian and I invited all staff out for a dinner to celebrate. And while it is not often that surgery leads to friendship, this surgery brought me close to Rod and his family.

## Reflection and relaxation

I realised later that my colleague, who had said I might kill my patient, meant that in putting an electrode into the inner ear there was a risk of meningitis, which had occurred very occasionally even with operations to remove the stapes bone from the middle ear and replace it with a prosthesis. This was the type of operation that he, I and others had been doing for some time. For that reason, I had been obsessively careful about sterility.

Ten days after the operation, Rod's incision had healed well, and I discharged him. I had decided we would then wait four weeks for his inner ear to recover from the surgery before he returned for vital testing. This should show if 10 years' work to develop multi-channel electrical stimulation of the cochlea and auditory nerve held promise for speech understanding. Nevertheless, it was such a relief to feel the first step was over. For the remainder of August, we returned to my parents' house and the countryside of my youth in Camden. This brought such peace and security, to walk back in time with my father and brother.

# The Canberra Times

*To serve the National City and through it the Nation*

Vol. 53. No. 15,837
Telephone 480066. Classifieds only 450555

THURSDAY, FEBRUARY 1, 1979

28 Pages. Price 14 cents*
Sydney and Melbourne 15c*

## Minister disagreed with loan advice, court told

A former Attorney-General, Mr Justice Murphy, had said that he considered the raising of a $US4,000 million overseas loan was for temporary purposes, a senior public servant told Queanbeyan Petty Sessions yesterday.

Mr D. J. Rose, a senior assistant secretary in the advisings division of the Attorney-General's Department, was giving evidence at a committal hearing of conspiracy charges against a former Prime Minister, Mr Whitlam, his deputy and former Treasurer, Dr Jim Cairns, and Mr Justice Murphy.

The charges brought in a private prosecution by a Sydney lawyer, Mr Danny Sankey, allege that the three men and the late Mr Rex Connor, a former Minister for Minerals and Energy, conspired to deceive the then Governor-General, Sir John Kerr, about the purposes of the $US4,000 million loan.

Mr Sankey alleges the four men committed the deception by advising Sir John in a Federal Executive Council minute of December 13, 1974, that the loan was for temporary purposes when they knew it was for financing large development projects of a permanent nature.

Mr Rose said Mr Justice Murphy, then Senator Lionel Murphy, had expressed his interpretation of the term "temporary purpose" at a meeting on December 13, 1974, which he [Mr Rose] and the secretary of the Attorney-General's Department, Sir Clarrie Harders, then Mr Harders, attended.

Mr Justice Murphy had considered the loan was a borrowing for temporary purposes under the meaning of Financial Agreements Act.

He had explained that the money was being borrowed to solve the looming unemployment and oil crises' — which were temporary problems. Mr Rose said he told Mr Justice Murphy that the traditional view was that temporary purposes related to short-term borrowings.

Mr Rose said Mr Justice Murphy did not seem to be very impressed with his [Mr Rose's] argument. Mr Rose said he had maintained his firm disagreement, and Mr Harders had said that he had had reservations.

At a meeting that afternoon in the Prime Minister's ante-room at Parliament House, Mr Justice Murphy had repeated his argument to the secretary of the Treasury, Sir Frederick Wheeler.

Sir Frederick said he did not presume to offer a view on the legal sense of the term, but thought it unlikely that Mr Justice Murphy's view would "live" in the Loan Council.

The Solicitor-General, Mr M. H. Byers, arrived, the meeting

## Bionic hearing

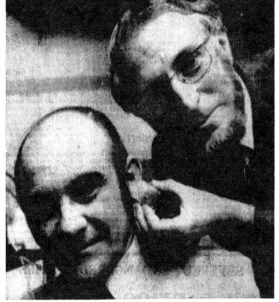

Professor G. M. Clark holds a "bionic ear" against the ear of Mr Rod Saunders, the first man to receive the implant. — Picturegram.

## University team develops world's first 'bionic ear'

### By PETER GOLDIE

An Australian bio-engineering team has developed a "bionic ear".

The device, which could benefit Australia's 10,000 and the world's four million profoundly or totally deaf, would sell on the commercial market for about $5,000.

The Minister for Productivity, Mr Macphee, announced yesterday expenditure of $400,000 for the first part of a two-phase program for the commercial development of the device which converts normal sounds into electronic impulses.

The impulses are scattered along a pattern of 10 electrodes implanted along the minute auditory nerve, stimulating electronic "sounds".

The Government grant for further research comes after $300,000 and 60 man-years of effort were spent on research and development of the device by Melbourne University's Department of Otolaryngology.

Working with the university team of graduate bio-engineers, Professor G. M. Clark developed the device over eight years. The services of the former Weapons Research Establishment and Telecom laboratories provided the technology which enabled the team to beat United States and French experts to the breakthrough.

A Melbourne man who lost his hearing as a result of head injuries received in a traffic accident in January, 1977, became the first test patient for the device when doctors implanted the "gold box" in his mastoid bone behind the ear.

Since the operation in August last year the team has determined that Mr Rod Saunders, 48, of Dandenong, can perceive at least six vowel sounds. This could improve as he learns to "interpret" the electronic impulses.

A statement issued in Canberra yesterday by Mr Mac-

phee placed great emphasis on the commercial development of the device, suggesting that the overseas market could provide "important economic benefits in employment and export sales".

Australian firms will be invited to participate in a project organised by the Department of Productivity and the Australian Industrial Research and Development Incentives Board which will undertake a detailed market study.

Money will also be made available to Melbourne University to continue further developments of the concept.

While the current experiments are being carried out on a group of selected patients Dr Clark sees no reason why, when fully developed, the bionic ear could not be implanted in children. There are no medical reasons why any deaf person could not receive the implant.

### 'He heard some sounds'

During one of Mr Rod Saunders' frequent visits

tralia's totally deaf, he could once hear.

It was in August last year

thing was really going to come out of the operation".

Inside the little gold box

## Vietnam cannot run wild: Deng

WASHINGTON, Wednesday (AAP-Reuter). — The Chinese Deputy Prime Minister, Mr Deng, has told US Senators, "We cannot allow Vietnam to run wild everywhere".

Mr Deng, answering questions at a closed session with the Senate Foreign Relations Committee yesterday, was asked if China might invade Vietnam because of tensions between the communist neighbours after the overthrow of the Peking-backed Government in Kampuchea.

"We cannot allow Vietnam to run wild everywhere", Mr Deng said. "In the interest of world peace and stability and in the interest of our own country, we may be forced to do what we do not like to do".

Most of his comments were made public by senators after the meeting.

Mr Deng accused the Soviet Union of backing Vietnam in Kampuchea and he later made his first public attack on the Soviet Union since arriving in the US on Sunday.

Speaking during a visit to the National Gallery of Art, Mr Deng referred to the overthrow of the Pot Government in Kampuchea syaing, "With the full backing of the Soviet Union, Vietnam is brazenly subjecting democratic Kampuchea to a massive armed aggression.

"Europe, too, is overshadowed by the threat

BANGKOK, Wednesday (AAP-AP). — Vietnam accused Chinese troops today of invading a Vietnamese northern border province, killing two patrolmen and wounding many others.

The Voice of Vietnam Radio, monitored in Bangkok, said the incident had occurred on Tuesday when more than 50 Chinese soldiers had attacked a Vietnamese patrol unit in area of Lang Son Province, 210 kilometres north of Hanoi. The Chinese had taken a Vietnamese rifle.

Thousands of Chinese troops had been sent into areas of the northern province over the past three days, causing tension to mount sharply at the frontier.

of war. It is very evident the hegemonist expansion is the main source of turmoil in all parts of the world. The zealous pushing of a global strategy for world domination by the hegemonists cannot but increase the danger of a new world war".

"Hegemony" is Peking's term for what it sees as Soviet global expansionist ambitions.

Mr Deng, the first communist Chinese leader to visit Washington, spent much of the day in discussion with President Carter and congressional leaders.

## Military aid 'to Pot'

BANGKOK, Wednesday (AAP-AP). — China is sending military supplies to the forces of toppled Prime Minister Mr Pot inside Kampuchea using Chinese ships and at least one offshore island to help fuel the six-week-old Kampuchean war, according to independent sources among Indochina analysts in Bangkok.

The operation off the south-western coast of Kampuchea fulfils a promise made by Mr Deng to continue aiding Peking's allies in face of invasion by Vietnamese troops and their Kampuchean allies.

One analyst said a coral island near the coastline had been heavily fortified with bunkers, anti-aircraft weapons and storage areas and was being manned by a number of Chinese advisers.

The island was identified as Khemara Phu Min, the name also given to the adjacent coastal area which rises from a maze of islands, bays and estuaries to the highest mountain ranges in Kampuchea.

Other sources confirmed that the Chinese had mounted a resupply operation to the Pot troops.

The coastline and the rugged Cardamon and Elephant Ranges beyond it had earlier been identified as one stronghold of the Pot forces.

On January 9, two days after the capture of Phnom Penh, Mr Deng had told US senators visiting Peking that China would continue to assist the Pot regime and Kampuchean forces in Kampuchea and that China did not regard the fall of Phnom Penh as the end of the struggle.

Some observers in Bangkok say that Peking might not believe the Vietnamese and the Government they installed in Phnom Penh can be defeated but that continuing conflict in Kampuchea would drain Hanoi's already meagre resources and weaken its pro-Soviet neighbour.

Khemara Phu Min island is four kilometres square with shallow coral beds on the landward side but a deeper approach from the sea side.

It is between Thai waters and the island of Kong.

## N. Korea 'to end war of words'

HONG KONG, Wednesday (AAP-Reuter). — North Korea announced today that it would stop its propaganda war against South Korea as a first step toward ending hostility between the two countries.

## AWU to seek new wage rises

SYDNEY: The Australian

# CHAPTER TWELVE

# Fundamental discoveries of speech and two Eureka moments

## Commencing studies

On returning to Melbourne, I realised that we would have to work fast to see if what I had promised—speech understanding for profoundly deaf Rod Saunders—would occur by the end of the year. It would be an extremely difficult task to code complex speech signals for them to be meaningful.

I was running out of money for all staff, as there was now no telethon, and I had not yet been successful with a National Health and Medical Research Council of Australia (NHMRC) grant application. I only had funds from a charity, the Ramaciotti Foundation, to keep engineer Ian Forster till the end of the year. Ian had found his position so insecure he had arranged to leave shortly after the new year and establish himself in Switzerland.

Four weeks after surgery in mid-September 1978, Rod came for the perceptual tests on electrical stimulation to see if we could code speech for it to be understood.

We had a unique opportunity to discover how speech is understood by the brain, and it would be a world first. So, I minimised my other responsibilities to work closely with budding psychophysicist Jo Tong as he completed his PhD on the modelling of cochlear function supervised by Dr Cecil Pengilley from Mechanical Engineering. Jim Patrick and Ian Forster, who had joined the team from Electrical Engineering, also played an invaluable role in managing the equipment and became well-versed in what was evolving at the clinical level.

**In 1979, the Australian Government awarded a grant to commercially develop the University of Melbourne cochlear implant.**

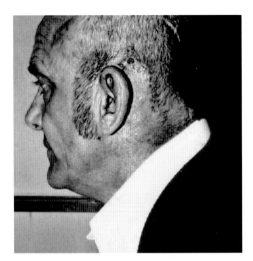

**Rod Saunders four weeks after his surgery, on returning for initial tests to see how to code speech.**

With Rod's surgical recovery, I had passed the point of no return. I was committed to discovering how speech could be coded. Although in my pre-operative discussions with Rod it was not guaranteed, he had trust and expectations that we could achieve it for him. No one was sure what sensations would be experienced with electrical stimulation, and scientists and clinicians, like physiologist Merle Lawrence and audiologist Ed Fowler, were very sceptical. (Read more about this in Chapter 5.)

So, the crucial perceptual tests began when I lined up the transmitting coil over where I believed the receiving coil on Rod's package lay under the swelling. (There was no magnet then to align the coils.) He heard nothing, and that was so disappointing to us all. I went home that night and prayed earnestly to God for guidance. Jim Patrick and other engineers then set about checking the electronic test equipment, as I believed the failure wasn't biological because of the finding of our earlier pre-operative electrical stimulation of his inner ear. But in a couple of days after the equipment was checked, Rod still only heard his tinnitus.

I had chosen Rod because he seemed unflappable. This trait was sorely needed now. And then, at the end of the week, to my delight, the engineers found the problem was simply due to a loose connection! So, Rod first heard on 18 September 1978.

## Press announcement

When the first heart transplant in Australia was carried out at St Vincent's Hospital in Sydney, there was press turmoil. Reporters even climbed up the wall to take shots through the operating theatre window. As I was also trying to break new ground, I was careful to avoid media attention. I did not want exaggerated reports of success or failure till we had carefully evaluated the situation. Fortunately, it soon became appropriate to let the press know after Rod first heard sounds. After that, they became very interested in the work. Many reports from all around the world have been archived and listed by the NLA and the *Encyclopaedia of Australian Science*.

## What did simple stimuli sound like?

Now that Rod could hear, a key question was: What would stimuli sound like to him? Did they have pitch, and did the pitch vary from high at the high frequency or basal end of the cochlea to low at the low or apical end of the cochlea? I said Rod could distinguish different pitch-like sounds when a continuum of varying sites around the cochlea was stimulated. But it was odd that instead of hearing pure tones as I was expecting, Rod heard sounds that varied from sharp at the high frequency end of the cochlea to dull at the low frequency end. This phenomenon needed more study and underscored the need for multi-channel stimulation. One person who was very interested in the answer to these questions was my former student Rick Hallworth, in Texas. He was a mechanical engineer who had done a Master of Engineering degree with Cecil Pengilley and me on a thin film electrode array for the place coding of frequency.

The distinctions in sounds were best described as timbre, although they did have pitch-like elements. Timbre is the quality of a sound that allows two musical instruments playing the same note and loudness to be distinguished. The timbre experienced was consistent with the psychoacoustics of normal hearing in which differences in timbre can be predicted from the frequency content or spectrum. This suggested that the distinction in timbre experienced was due to the simultaneous electrical stimulation of groups of neurons transmitting frequencies on a place-coding basis. From 18 September till 27 November 1978, Jo Tong and I studied the sensations experienced by Rod for simple single or dual stimuli to see how they could underlie speech codes.

Angela Marshall, now a lecturer in our postgraduate course in audiology and well-versed in audiological procedures, had returned from overseas on 7 October 1978 and collaborated with us. First, we wanted to check out Rod's auditory memory, and wondered whether he could recognise familiar tunes. So, we played our national anthem on a single electrode. Immediately,

Rod stood to attention, as was the custom. In doing so, he accidentally pulled all his leads out. Hence, we have no recording. After settling him down, we played the Australian folk anthem *Waltzing Matilda*. Again, he had no trouble following the tune from the rhythm but found it hard to sing the higher notes.

## The perception of pitch and loudness

Psychophysical (perceptual) studies were next carried out using simple electrical stimuli to discover how he perceived pitch for rate and place of electrical stimulation, and loudness for current intensity. I fully expected rate of stimulation to be perceived as pitch up to quite high speech frequencies, due to the nerve fibres firing in time with the stimuli. At first, this was supported by finding that rate of stimulation was perceived as a true pitch sensation, but unfortunately rate pitch could only be discriminated at low rates, as reflected in the neural responses seen with my electrophysiological research at the UoS and later with behavioural tests on the experimental animal, as well as perceptual studies on Rod later on.

The finding on Rod was a good demonstration that as rate of stimulation was increased pitch reached a plateau at only 200 pulses/s. Therefore, rate was suited to code for the low frequencies in voicing, but not mid-to-high frequencies for consonants.

Therefore, I became keener to explore the perception of place pitch, and this was to lead to successful multi-channel speech coding. Although place of stimulation was primarily perceived as varying from sharp (basal turn) to dull (apical turn) timbres, it did have pitch qualities. The perceptions of pitch for rate and place of stimulation, although separate sensations, influenced each other. This suggests that in the brain there is pitch perception integration for temporal and place pitch.

So, in view of the initial findings for the perception of place of stimulation, Jo Tong and I explored this phenomenon in more detail. We then considered it important that we rank timbre on a place basis to develop an effective speech code, with timbre being ranked according to site of stimulation. In addition to pitch, loudness was studied. It rose rapidly over a 6-dB range in current amplitude. This was narrower than the 60-dB range for acoustic clicks but was still usable when sound was compressed electronically.

I viewed understanding the perception of simple stimuli, such as rate and place of stimulation, as essential prerequisites for speech coding. But as funding would dry up by early 1979, I knew we would have to strike gold and achieve a code for speech understanding by the end of 1978 to successfully appeal for further funds to finish the journey.

## First clue to speech coding: My first Eureka moment

At one of Rod's test sessions, I was very excited when he not only described a sensation as sharp or dull, but also as a vowel. That was my first Eureka moment (an exclamation first attributed to Archimedes on discovering the principle of buoyancy). When we stimulated the high frequency region of the cochlea, Rod described the sound as sharp, but he also heard the vowel "i" as in "seat," or "ɪ" as in "sit." On the other hand, for a stimulus at the low frequency region, it sounded dull and he heard it as "ɒ" as in "hot," or "ɔ" as in "cord." This relationship showed a correlation between the second formant (F2) frequency and the frequency coded for site of stimulation.

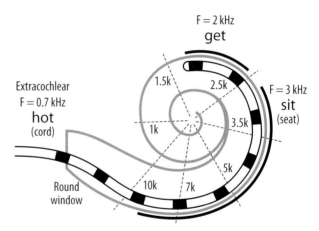

**The perception of vowels versus site of stimulation in the first patient's cochlea.**

That first Eureka moment led to the first speech code that gave a patient the ability to understand speech with electrical stimulation alone. To help us further understand how the electrical stimuli were being coded as vowels, I invited Bruce Millar, with his strong background in speech perception at the University of Keele, then at the Australian National University, to help investigate the question. He stayed at our home for part of his visit to Melbourne between 1 October and 24 November 1978. We had scientific discussions and he participated in family activities.

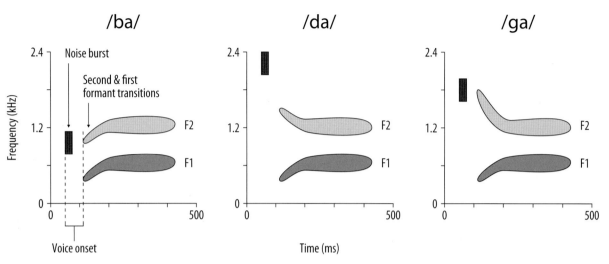

**The first (F1) and second (F2) formant transitions and initial noise burst for plosives.**

We also searched the literature with particular reference to the work of Gunnar Fant, who had first emphasised the importance of formants in speech and whom I had visited in Stockholm in February 1976 when on study leave. Close examination of Rod's responses helped establish there was a correlation between site of stimulation and the second formants in speech, especially for vowels.

Formants which are resonant frequencies arise from the shape of the vocal tract, as discussed in Chapter 9. As Gunnar Fant and team had shown for the vocal tract, there is not a simple relationship, but they are significant cues for intelligibility. There are first (F1), second (F2) and third formant (F3) codes and even higher formant frequencies that could be reproduced for speech understanding. The F2 frequencies are mid-to-high frequency sounds, and most important for intelligibility. The findings also demonstrated a strong relation between brain neural activity and our conscious experiences of speech.

It was during this time that I also noticed that stimulating the most basal or high frequency electrode produced a low pitch sound or dull timbre, which did not fit the place coding of frequency. However, I resolved this dilemma as pitch studies demonstrated Rod's electrode bundle had slipped out 10 mm. From the findings, the current must have passed around the auditory nerve and excited the low frequency fibres that wrap around the nerve. Thus, our findings still supported the concept that the way forward would be multi-channel electrical stimulation using the place coding of frequency.

At this stage, to develop an effective speech code, we needed a system that could also code consonants, which carry 80% of speech information. Speech studies have demonstrated that consonants are of shorter duration than vowels, vary more rapidly over time and have frequency transitions that are important for their identification (as illustrated for the plosives in "ba," "da" and "ga" in the figure on the previous page). For this

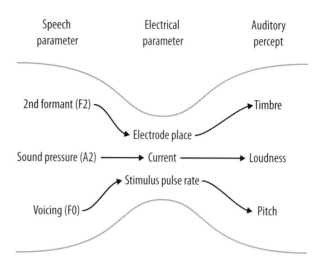

**The speech parameters transmitted through the electro-neural "bottleneck" for speech perception. This became the first successful speech processing strategy (code) to achieve running speech understanding without lipreading assistance.**

reason, I arranged for Angela Marshall to explore the perception of complex stimuli and, in particular, the F2 transitions.

Then, from Friday 20 October to Wednesday 25 October, Angela, as recorded in her protocol book, presented stimuli where the onset of stimuli on two or three electrodes was varied in time (2 ms to 3 ms) or the rate (140 pulses/s and 150 pulses/s). In this case, Rod heard a word that sounded like "bulup." We attributed this to the summed energy pattern produced by a time delay in the stimuli of 2 ms to 3 ms, or 150 pulses/s and 140 pulses/s over a 200 ms interval. The energy pattern for the word "bulup" is similar. It demonstrated that for more sophisticated strategies, we could expect the brain to perceive and process rapid shifts in place of stimulation.

At this stage, it was premature and too complex to produce specific codes for each phoneme in speech. But as I had told Rod, we would develop a code that would help him in his daily life as soon as possible; the evidence from our animal behavioural and human psychophysics studies indicated it was more straightforward to extract F2, an important cue for intelligibility, and code it as place of stimulation. We would also use rate for coding the low rates of voicing (F0) across the F2 electrodes and use current level for the amplitude (A0). This, in effect, would code important speech information for transmission through the electro-neural "bottleneck" to the brain.

## A physiological speech code

While the second formant (F0/F2/A0) code was being put together in software, from 27 November till 1 December 1978, I was keen to evaluate a physiologically-based speech processing strategy, a discipline in which I had been steeped when doing my PhD. The speech processor was developed by Rod Laird for his master's degree in the Electrical Engineering Department with supervision by Paul Lynn, David Dewhurst and me.

The strategy modelled basilar membrane motion in the cochlea and the fine timing of auditory nerve firing. But the results were not satisfactory. We assumed this was due to the electrical fields produced by the code overlapping in place and time to give unpredictable variations in loudness. Thus, one could not hope to take a speech signal and present it as a series of electrical stimuli without some form of pre-processing, an understanding of the perceptions obtained or a knowledge of the spread of current within the cochlea.

## Second Eureka moment:
## Speech understanding with electrical stimulation

Until 14 December 1978, Angela Marshall presented Rod with closed sets of syllables and words using the F0/F2/A0 code that helped train his brain to recognise speech.

As Rod was doing very well with these tests, I asked Angela to present him open sets of words using electrical stimulation alone. This was a very hard test. They could be any words from his vocabulary and must not have been specially practised. She was reluctant to do so at first, as she did not think he would succeed, and believed it might discourage him. If he did succeed, it would be a better result than for single-channel implants and demonstrate its value in understanding running speech. So, I was persistent. Angela presented the open set list, and Rod got approximately 10% correct. The positive result had not been achieved before with classical word tests and was the priceless pearl I was searching for. It indicated that Rod should be able to use the code in his everyday life, and with improved engineering of the speech processor, do even better.

It was my second Eureka moment; it was the moment I had been working so hard to achieve, and for so long. I was so overcome that I went quietly into the next-door laboratory and burst into tears of joy. It was worth all the blood, sweat and tears.

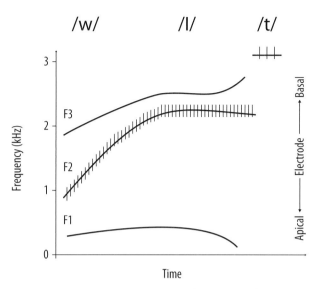

Inaugural second formant (F0/F2/A0) speech code for the word "wit" (1978–79). Continuous lines are: first (F1), second (F2) and third formant (F3) frequencies. Vertical bars are electrical pulses coding voicing across electrodes coding the second formant frequency by place of stimulation.

Towards the end of 1978, I was overjoyed we had just done the impossible. We had discovered how to code speech for a severely/profoundly deaf person by electrical stimulation of the auditory brain. But Christmas and the summer holidays were fast approaching, and I would be unable to establish the findings till the new year. With this and all other important results it was my dictum that it was better for us to prove ourselves wrong than for someone else to do so. I would therefore have to wait with unusual patience till I knew whether my application to the Australian Government for funding was successful. This would allow me to appoint an able audiologist to carry out more extensive word tests, as Angela was needed for lecturing.

## Selecting an audiologist for testing Rod if grant application were successful

I realised how important it was to have intelligent and versatile staff in all areas of the work. This was to be a job for those in the top 10% of their field. Hence, as the chief examiner for our course in audiology, immediately after the examiners' meeting in November 1978, I concluded that Lois Martin was an outstanding audiologist and would be just the person to select to take charge of our patients. If I did it today it would be politically incorrect, but I raced after Lois down Morrison Place and offered her the job on the basis that I would receive the grant. I was delighted that she accepted on those conditions.

## Patents

In 1976, we had created the first implantable multi-channel cochlear prosthesis and probably the most complex package of electronics for implantation in a person, and I felt it should be patented. At the time, this was not a common practice at the university. There was, however, a patent committee with a senior industrialist in the chair to advise. I was directed to a patent attorney and had to spend time in helping to write the inventions. The design of the receiver-stimulator was difficult to distinguish from prior attempts, but our electrode bundle, and certainly the speech code, were unique, and patenting was easier.

## Publication of results

Before Christmas, we had very important data suggesting that speech coding would be possible. Dr Dean Beaumont, editor of the *Journal of the Otolaryngological Society of Australia*, agreed to publish it in the 1978 edition. So, I was in a mad rush to write the paper on behalf of our team before the holidays.

The paper reported that rate of stimulation was perceived as pitch, but this rose more rapidly compared to sound frequency. At 50 pulses/s, the pitch was equivalent to a sound of 50 Hz, and at 200 pulses/s to one of 3,000 Hz. There was also a change in timbre or pitch in line with the tonotopic arrangement of the frequency responses around the basal turn. Both findings suggested that as processing of the signal by the hair cells in the cochlea was absent, direct electrical stimulation of the nerves accounted for the differences. A most exciting finding was the fact that Rod heard different vowels when varying frequency sites in the cochlea were stimulated. We concluded that the most appropriate design for a speech processor would be a code that extracted the formants for vowels and consonants.[46]

**Audiologist, Angela Marshall talks with Rod Saunders at the Bionic Ear Institute in 2003. It was Angela who introduced Rod to me in 1977. Pam Dawson, the key paediatric audiologist who later tested the implanted children, is in the background.**

## Relaxation

After all the effort and stress associated with it, I was relieved to go with my wife and children to Kiama and see my family again. As well as relaxing by camping with the children, there was some excitement one time when the big set of waves best described as dumpers at Kendall's beach became huge. I asked the lifesaver if he thought I should go out. He assented, and so I did. The waves got bigger, and all the surfers left the water, but I did not. The only thing to do was to swim out further where the waves were not breaking. But I lost my nerve and waved my hand for rescue. The young guy came out immediately, put the belt around me and dragged me in. Too bad I was dumped in the process. He had saved me! Some years later, he recognised me in the shopping mall at Kiama, and I had an opportunity to thank him again.

# CHAPTER THIRTEEN

# Facilitating the industrial development of the multi-channel implant

It was great news to learn on 31 January 1979 that the Minister for Productivity, the Honourable Ian Macphee AO, had announced the Australian pacemaker firm Telectronics, a subsidiary of Nucleus, was selected, ahead of major companies including Siemens, to develop a bionic ear.

## Managing the grant

David Dewhurst and I would be the UoM representatives on the government steering committee to monitor progress and be accountable for the use of funds. This meant frequent trips to Sydney for committee meetings at Telectronics. The industrial development of the multi-channel implant was to be undertaken in four phases from 1979 to 1985.[47] The Australian Government wanted it to succeed, and they kept bureaucracy to a minimum. It was the best-managed large grant I ever received.

The grant enabled me to confirm the appointment of audiologist Lois Martin from our School of Audiology to help provide as much objective evidence as possible on the communication benefits of our new strategy on Rod and an additional two patients. An analysis of the data should also show why it was so successful.

Now I had a chance to validate my second Eureka moment: that the inaugural F0/F2/A0 speech code gave open-set speech understanding, even using electrical stimulation alone. Audiologist Lois Martin did so conclusively in 1979, firstly with lipreading and then electrical stimulation alone.

**Rod Saunders using his wearable speech processor. The initial speech processing was done with software on the standalone computer in the background.**

## Funding difficulties

However, the government had not given enough money to complete the silicon chips for the industrial development of the implant. To find a way, I went to the Weapons Research Laboratory in Adelaide to see what facilities they had, and whether they might be of help on a *pro bono* basis. In those days, the Commonwealth Scientific Industrial Research Organisation (CSIRO) and other government bodies such as the Weapons Research Laboratories had generous funding to help good projects, and ours fulfilled that requirement.

Prior to this visit, I had contacted the new Minster for Productivity, Senator Kevin Newman, who commenced his portfolio at the beginning of 1978. As soon as I arrived in Adelaide, I received a message that Kevin Newman would be in Melbourne on his way home to Hobart, and could I meet him. So, I caught the next flight back to Melbourne. I was pleased to meet Kevin and hear the good news that the government would increase its funding.

## Learning the range of communication benefits of the second formant (F0/F2/A0) speech code

In learning the range of communication benefits with the F0/F2/A0 speech code experienced by Rod, we also discovered how complex stimuli that are important for speech perception were being coded. With Lois Martin and a second audiologist Peter Busby, I participated in presenting a variety of standard audiological tests, and with Jo Tong and Ray Black, a series of psychophysical and electrophysiological studies. By learning how speech was coded by electrical stimulation of the brain I considered we should be able to improve speech perception for patients so that they would be able to converse over the telephone and engage in everyday conversation.

This involved analysing how well different speech cues such as voicing, nasality, affrication, duration and place of articulation (in the latter case from lips together, tongue to teeth and tongue to palate) were coded with electrical stimulation. The tests showed the F0/F2/A0 speech code gave poorest results for place of articulation. As place of articulation is a most important acoustic cue for consonants, this indicated where further research should be directed.

## Presentation of results and scepticism

By the first half of 1979 I had well-established data on the benefits of the multi-channel cochlear implant, though it was still in software and only on one patient. After presenting the encouraging results on Rod Saunders in 1979 to a meeting of scientists, I was surprised at the scepticism. One member said he detected that the voice and lips were not in synchrony, and therefore that I had doctored the presentation.

I also gave a talk on these findings to the elite otologists in the Toynbee Club—my first scientific presentation. At the end, there was silence till one member, Dr Barrie Scrivener, stood and applauded. Barrie had been my ear, nose and throat mentor at the Royal Prince Alfred Hospital (RPAH), and an old boy of The Scots College. Much later, my colleagues in the Toynbee Club graciously asked me to give the keynote address at their 50-year celebrations, and at the end of my talk they asked a very pertinent question: What would I have done if it had all failed? My only answer was that I would have felt I should resign, as people had been hinting.

## Implanting more patients

Halfway through 1979, it was time to implant two additional patients as required by the Commonwealth grant to show whether the implant had a wider application for industrial development, and that it was not a unique code applying to one person only.

George Watson, aged 63 years, was the second person to be implanted on 17 July 1979. He had had no useful hearing for 17 years after a bomb blast. Surprisingly, at his second test session, he had the conscious experience of speech. My office was just up from the test room, and I shall not forget the excitement as staff rushed down to buy the paper to read to George. After a practice run, he could repeat nearly word for word a news item. In addition, his overall results were similar to those of my first patient Rod.

In George's case the results indicated that the neural representation for consciousness can lie dormant for 17 years. This suggests that consciousness is due to the activation of electrical circuitry and/or the molecular structure of the central nervous system. I believe we are more than walking electrical circuits, but at the very least we are interlinked biomolecules.

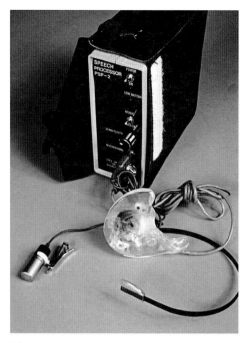

The wearable speech processor (silver box) that used the University of Melbourne second formant (F0/F2/A0) speech code, seen alongside our initial headset and transmitter coil.

A third patient had her operation soon afterwards, but in those days the polytome x-rays did not give a clear picture of the degree of bone formation in her cochleae that often develops after meningitis. We operated on the worse ear, but we could not make a pathway through the bone for the electrode bundle to pass any distance, and so I decided to abandon the operation and wait till we could implant her other relatively good ear with a proven device. She, George Watson and I were very disappointed, especially as that opportunity never arose.

I found a replacement, Mrs D. Although she had good psychophysical results, because of a condition she had, I had to explant her device. This was not a good start to the program, but I was determined to obtain as much information as possible from Rod and then George, until George's device failed!

The studies on Rod and George confirmed that more than one profoundly deaf person could obtain some useful speech understanding using electrical stimulation alone, and it certainly gave significant benefits when combined with lipreading. These were the first reports on the communication benefits of an electrical stimulus code using standardised audiological tests, not limited sets, as were being used for some single-channel implants. As a result, our findings could be compared and validated with those from other centres. They also showed that the successful code in the first patient was not a unique one that I had chanced upon, as was being suggested. They also demonstrated the multi-channel code was superior to that of any single-channel implant code.[48]

## Wearable speech processor

While Rod was being tested with the speech code using computer software, it became necessary after receiving the public interest grant from the government to demonstrate that our speech coding strategy could be developed electronically as a speech processor small enough to be worn. I had approached David Dewhurst in Engineering, and he said one of his students could implement it as a device the size of a sewing machine that could be wheeled around. I was adamant that would not do. We would have to find a better way.

The road to that better way started in 1978 when I received a phone call from Peter Seligman, who had seen our publicity and said he would like a position with our team. I explained that as yet, I had no money, and would let him know if a position arose. I had a strong feeling he would be the one to help us and said to Margaret, "I think this man will be the answers to my prayers." As Peter writes in his book,[49] when his son received a phone call from me enquiring after Dr Seligman, he told me there were "no doctors in the house." Not to be put off, when Peter came to the phone, I asked him to join the group, as money was now available. He was confident his commercial experience with Westinghouse brakes would allow him to achieve a design for a wearable speech processor by cutting corners, so to speak, something perhaps slightly foreign to the university's way of thinking.

## Evaluation of the wearable speech processor "silver box"

By the middle of 1979, Peter Seligman, working closely with Jim Patrick, had developed a wearable speech processor that implemented the UoM F0/F2/A0 speech code. It was the size of a binocular case, and we called it the "silver box," as distinct from the "gold box," the implant itself. I could not wait to be able to demonstrate its use in everyday life, so rushed Rod to a newsagent across Victoria Parade and photographed him on 17 September 2001 buying a magazine.

To help convince the sceptics of the wearable speech processor's value, I then took movies of its use in everyday life, choosing a domestic scene with Rod's wife in a kitchen and another with daughters and friend at their home.

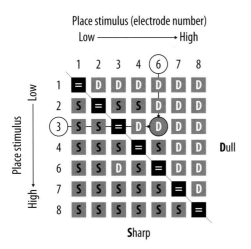

Place stimulus (electrode number)

Low ——————→ High

**The ranking of pitch (as timbre) with place of stimulation. For example, on the vertical axis the more apical electrode (electrode 3) for low frequencies was duller (D) than the more basal, high frequency electrode (electrode 6) on the horizontal axis which was sharper (S). Also, the duller and sharper ones lay on either side of the diagonal, indicating good ranking of timbre (1980–81).**

It made a great difference to Rod's life, and he returned willingly to our lab so that we could study what information our electrical stimulus code transmitted to his brain while he was using the wearable speech processor.

## Studies to determine why the second formant (F0/F2/A0) speech code was so successful

We had shown that place coding of frequency underpinned speech perception. But as place of stimulation was not perceived as pitch but timbre, I was keen to check that the changes in timbre could be perceived in an orderly way by stimulating electrodes along the length of the cochlea. The results obtained by Richard Dowell demonstrated good ranking of timbre which has become the basis for all multi-channel stimulation.

Consonants carry more information than vowels for speech identification (80%), and they are usually shorter in duration (25 ms) and vary more rapidly over time. It was important to learn how variations in rate and place of stimulation could be used to provide these cues, so using electrical stimulation we studied how Rod discriminated them over the short durations required. With rate of stimulation, Rod's ability to detect differences in frequency was poor when the duration of the stimulus was below 100 ms. Discrimination decreased from 240 pulses/s, 210 pulses/s, 180 pulses/s and 150 pulses/s compared to 150 pulses/s. This made rate of stimulation unsuitable for coding consonants. On the other hand, place of stimulation could be well discriminated down to the required duration of 25 ms. There was no change in discrimination as the site of stimulation varied from electrodes 4, 3, and 2 to base line 1 over 25 ms, 50 ms and 100 ms.

Therefore, F2 frequencies and other formants for understanding consonants were coded as place of stimulation. However, to distinguish voiced consonants such as "d" from unvoiced ones such as "t," rate of stimulation was used as it sounded voice-like. Furthermore, our behavioural studies showed that rate of stimulation could be perceived as pitch when low and high frequency regions of the cochlea were stimulated, and so could be used to code voicing for a range of stimulus sites.[50] In addition, we confirmed the relationship between

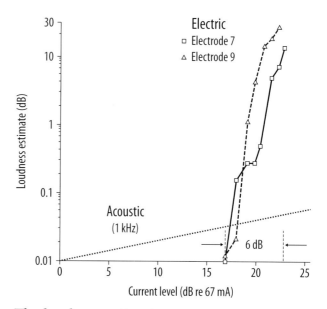

The loudness estimates are measured on the vertical axis and the current levels on the horizontal axis. The graphs for acoustic and electrical stimuli are shown (1979).

electrical current and loudness, so that we could ensure the stimuli were within the comfortable range.

The F0/F2/A0 speech code we had discovered on Rod in 1978 and then George in 1979 was validated using a series of standardised audiological tests. These demonstrated a marked improvement in communication, especially combined with lipreading, but also with electrical stimulation alone.

This was something not thought possible when I first commenced research. I was determined to provide solid objective data on speech results with our multi-channel code to confirm all our observations. The good mean scores for electrical stimulation alone were the first and best pieces of evidence that this code with multi-channel stimulation would help in all aspects of daily life. Our results for speech perception were reported in major conference proceedings and journals.[51]

Then, unfortunately, George's device started to fail towards the end of 1979 when a press conference had been scheduled to proceed. Fortunately, both patients got through unscathed.

I returned from summer holidays to find that George's device had failed completely. Before going off the air, he experienced some strange noises. Worse still, he had developed a hole through the skin (termed a "sinus") over the package, caused by pressure from falling asleep while lying on that side in bed. I had to treat this as it was infected. I decided, after carefully considering the pros and cons, that surgeon Rob Webb should cut the electrode off just near where it entered the inner ear and remove the package. The explanted package was treated like a piece of moon rock. Nucleus, through its fledgling company, was starting to develop a clinical trial device, and it was essential to know what went wrong. It turned out that the problem was due to stress fractures of the lead wire from small repeated body movements that fatigued the metal. I had seen this with my behavioural studies on cats, where their chewing movements resulted in metal fatigue, meaning we had to use multi-stranded wire to retain electrical conductivity. The finding came just in time for Nucleus to ensure that their device had coiled multi-stranded wire that was flipped back and forth a million times to ensure its safety.

## Partnership with industry for research and development

Working from 1979 with Nucleus/Telectronics Ltd as an industrial partner was a learning experience for me and I think also for the Australian Government. It was only the second time the government had funded a major research project for industrial development. The first time was exploiting the time reference scanning beam (TRSB), which was developed by CSIRO's Wild and Minnett, and shown to be better than the USA, UK and other European systems for aircraft landing.

I did not want our hard-earned ideas, expertise and technology dissipated, so when we received funding, I was determined to help make our development an Australian one. There was talk that the head office should be relocated to the USA for the main market because

Australia was isolated. On the committee, we were of one mind and said that we could not use taxpayers' money for the centre to be overseas. The successful tendering company, Nucleus/Telectronics, would have to develop their markets by establishing offices in other places, but the industrial knowhow had to stay in this country.

Paul Trainor, the controlling shareholder of Nucleus, was honourable. He played the game straight and was easy to relate to. He was a good judge of character and ability—important for successful outcomes with complicated research and development. From the beginning, he wanted me to agree that the development take place at Nucleus/Telectronics in the Lane Cove precinct in Sydney. My desire to have it in Melbourne, near the main research group at the university, was overruled, but I considered we would still have to play a very active role in the research and clinical program that I had built up over nine years. Paul next wanted my senior staff to relocate to Sydney for the transfer of knowledge quickly. He maintained that success in the market depended not only on having good patent protection but also on speed of delivery. Jim Patrick, our senior engineer, was happy to move, but Peter Seligman remained in Melbourne where he was close enough to carry out evaluations of the patients, enabling Peter to learn at an early stage what improvements in patient management were most needed.

Paul Trainor had many challenges which he shared with me from time to time. When he needed money from venture capitalists the two of us would go and speak to raise support. Paul called us "the Punch and Judy show". Jim Loughnan was company Director for Nucleus and had supervisory responsibilities for this new development in artificial hearing. David Money, an outstanding electrical engineer with the pacemaker firm, was appointed to be the first Chief Executive Officer. Maria Yetton agreed to lead a formal market survey, with assistance from Dr Michael Hirshorn, a medical graduate from the UoM with an MBA. Their first question was: What is the market size for something without real evidence it will even work?

I helped with information and gave an appraisal of the international otolaryngological field, which was quite new to all at Nucleus/Cochlear. Maria and Michael had many factors to consider: a cost-benefit analysis and an appraisal of the regulatory controls in each prospective country, the relative status of the research achievements of competitor groups (which do not always provide an accurate picture of their work) and whether the research would lead to a commercially marketable product. In the end, I was thrilled to learn that our UoM team was considered the best in the world and worth supporting. That helped justify my approach of doing good science and publishing in peer-reviewed journals so that clinicians knew they could trust our findings. For me it also meant I would need to go to many meetings in Sydney to help coordinate the industrial research.

## The alpha test centre at the University of Melbourne and the Royal Victorian Eye and Ear Hospital

At the UoM, we became the alpha test centre, which meant selecting and operating on our patients to ensure the engineering of the device incorporated the speech coding strategy and that it performed as well as our prototype before it was released for world distribution. This made me keener than ever to involve myself in all essential areas of the work and so feel comfortable the device had been well engineered for the best care of my patients. So we scrutinised our findings very carefully.

The results for a group of six patients from the UoM at the Cochlear Implant Clinic at the RVEEH were first evaluated for the Nucleus/Cochlear Ltd device developed industrially from the UoM's prototype. Working in pairs, Brian Pyman, Rob Webb, Quentin Bailey and I implanted those patients from September to December 1982. Brian and I had refined the original surgical approach by creating a circular recess in the mastoid bone for the stalk of the receiver-stimulator.[52]

Graham Carrick, the first patient, was 37 years of age and became severely/profoundly deaf at the age of five years after being given streptomycin for burns. He had an implant in his right ear on 14 September 1982. Three weeks later he had his first "switch on." When the currents in all the electrodes in Graham's cochlea were adjusted at comfortable levels, he was excited to be able to hear speech. One of the first things he did was to phone his mother to hear her voice again.

These Nucleus/Cochlear Ltd implants used the same coding strategy as the university's speech processor but selected information at twice the rate. There was some improvement in the perception of temporal speech features such as voicing. A significant number of our

**Holding the first Nucleus/Cochlear Ltd implant for clinical trial in my University of Melbourne office at the Royal Victorian Eye and Ear Hospital in 1982.**

subjects had useful open-set speech recognition for electrical stimulation alone. This was the goal I had set out to achieve and it became the gold standard by which to assess implant benefits. The well-controlled audiological results were reported on the first four patients in 1983 in the *Journal of the Acoustical Society of America*[53] and the *Medical Journal of Australia*.[54] They confirmed the results from the UoM's prototype coding strategy and speech processor.

This very positive result from our initial evaluation of the multi-channel device gave confidence in initiating a world trial for approval by the US Food and Drug Administration (FDA). By this time, Cochlear Ltd had been listed on the stock exchange and the multi-channel implant was to be trialled in the USA, Germany and Australia to demonstrate the range of benefits for people with various causes of deafness.

To help achieve that goal we implanted more post-linguistically deaf patients in Melbourne, and the results on 10 patients were reported in the *Australian and New Zealand Journal of Surgery* in 1984.[55] The study concluded that a multi-channel cochlear prosthesis is an appropriate device to help patients with a profound/total hearing loss. The results were especially encouraging as they confirmed our previous findings that some could use the device to communicate without the need to lipread, as, for example, on the telephone. Results on the first seven of these patients were also reported in *Acta Otolaryngologica* (Stockholm)[56] and eight in the *Annals of Otology, Rhinology and Laryngology*. These indicated that in six patients there was significant open-set speech discrimination without lipreading at levels not reported for single

Graham Carrick, the first patient to receive the Nucleus/ Cochlear Ltd multi-channel cochlear implant inserted by Brian Pyman and me at the Royal Victorian Eye and Ear Hospital on 12 September 1982. The device is shown being tested in the Univeristy of Melbourne Department of Otolaryngology by audiologist Richard Dowell.

electrode cochlear prostheses. All patients were using the pocket-sized speech processor Cochlear Ltd developed to incorporate the university's speech code. The underlying physiological, biological and speech science for the engineering of our multi-channel cochlear implant was fully described.

To further clarify the multi-channel cochlear implant's benefits, I arranged with two of our senior audiologists prior to our 1985 symposium to evaluate speech perception over the telephone for two patients. This was a simple way to demonstrate the cochlear implant's use in everyday life without the need to lipread. Patient #4 in the group achieved a 47% score in the Central Institute for the Deaf's (CID's) Everyday Sentence test and these results were published in the *Journal of Laryngology and Otology* in March 1985.[57] This was the first time a cochlear implant had been shown to be effective for useful conversations on the telephone. With more information added since to the code, many more patients now have useful interactive conversations face to face and over the telephone.

My next question was: Would the cochlear implant code for other formant-based languages? Fortunately, Melbourne is a very multicultural city with people from diverse backgrounds. It was not difficult to find deaf people who had migrated from European countries. I was relieved to learn their results were comparable to those for English speakers.

But what about the benefits for the many from Asian countries with a tonal language? With a language such as Mandarin, meaning is achieved by varying the way the voiced pitch glides up and down. As our speech code had been designed to use rate of stimulation to convey voicing and place of stimulation for the formant frequencies in consonants and vowels, I was not overly confident of success. But we had a 19-year-old profoundly deaf Chinese man from Malaysia who was a suitable subject, and I had recently employed doctor Xiang Xu from China. I suggested to Xiang that he establish tests equivalent to those in English for assessing our patient. I was amazed at the results, even without lipreading assistance, and showed them at our first International Cochlear Implant Symposium and Workshop in 1985.[58] They were so impressive that Professor Bob White from Stanford University jokingly commented: "All people having cochlear implants should learn Mandarin."

But there was still scepticism that our multi-channel system was really better than single-channel devices for formant-based languages. Some clinics across the world continued implanting single-channel devices that could give no speech recognition, only awareness of sound.

However, this debate was finally put to rest in 1985 at our first International Cochlear Implant Symposium in Melbourne when Dr Bruce Gantz from Iowa presented the results of their independent analysis of four strategies: two single-channel and two multi-channel cochlear implants funded by the us National Institutes of Health (NIH) and Lions Clubs International (LCI). Four people used the Los Angeles/House/3M single-channel design; three were implanted with the Vienna/Hochmair intracochlear single-channel prosthesis; five patients wore the Melbourne/Clark/Nucleus 21-channel design; and five patients were fitted with the Utah/Eddington/Symbion 4-channel device. The results showed that the multi-channel systems provided more useful information for speech understanding than the single-channel designs.[59]

It was fortuitous that we were included in this significant study. Only a couple of years before in 1983, Professor Brian McCabe from Iowa had been the Guest of Honour at the local

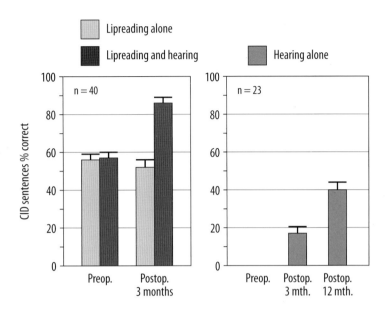

LEFT: Central Institute for the Deaf sentence scores for the Nucleus/Cochlear Ltd multi-channel implant. **RIGHT:** The 40% score for a group of 12 months' post-operative patients for electrical stimulation alone. This meant they could have a useful conversation without the need to lipread, results that were generally considered impossible before we reported them.

Otolaryngological Society meeting at which I presented our most recent results. These must have impressed him, as no sooner did he return to the USA than I received a call from him asking us to be involved in a study by Iowa and of course I agreed. Brian arranged for his young protégé Dr Bruce Gantz to visit our centre and learn what we were doing and how best to insert our implant. Nevertheless, as Bruce did not reveal his findings prior to his presentation at our 1985 international conference, I went along with bated breath wondering what his findings would be. I need not have worried for it was clear the debate was nearing an end and my decision to do multi-channel stimulation was vindicated.

Finally, the results for a wider group of 40 patients in the study for the US FDA at centres in the USA, Germany and Australia were first reported by Webb, Dowell et al. at the 34th meeting of the Otolaryngological Society of Australia at Perth in September 1985.[60] The average CID sentence scores went from 52% for lipreading alone to 87% for lipreading combined with electrical stimulation using the multi-channel formant code. We showed that in 25 of the patients who had a one-year follow up, the mean scores went from 16.2% at three months (top score

58%) to 40% at 12 months (top score of 86%) for electrical stimulation alone. These findings were the first to confirm in a large group of patients the good results for a speech code with multi-channel stimulation.[61] They also clearly showed that multi-channel electrical stimulation could provide everyday speech understanding with electrical stimulation alone, declared by professionals to be improbable or impossible, but now the gold standard for all cochlear implants to achieve.

Funding from the Australian Government continued, but the government was adamant this had to stop when FDA approval was obtained, and we at the UoM, including Richard Dowell as Head of Audiology, were able to play a crucial role in the cochlear implant's evaluation by the FDA. The findings, when collated with background and safety material, allowed the Nucleus/Cochlear Ltd implant to be approved by the US FDA late in 1985. This was the first multi-channel implant to be approved by the US FDA or any world regulatory body for the restoration of speech understanding in adults who had lost hearing before becoming severely/profoundly deaf.

## Criticisms

Over the years, there were three groups of critics of any attempt to restore speech understanding with electrical stimulation of the brain. These were: scientists, clinicians and the Signing Deaf Community. The scientists were the first to criticise us on the grounds that using electrical stimulation to restore speech understanding was contrary to current research findings, and I learned that the way science worked was to see whether a new hypothesis or outcome can be proved wrong before it can be accepted. However, the scientists were the first to recognise the multi-channel cochlear implant's merits, and I was asked to give presentations to the New York Academy of Science,[62] at a satellite conference on mechanisms of hearing at Monash University in 1983 and for an international Physiology Society meeting in Sydney.

The second group, surgical colleagues, had two reasons for criticism. Firstly, there was the risk of middle ear infection spreading to the brain and leading to meningitis. Secondly, they were influenced by the negative opinion of some leading surgeons and scientists about results from single-channel implants. But in time they were gracious in realising the multi-channel cochlear implant's benefits and invited me to organise a whole cochlear implant component for the World Otolaryngological Societies Congress, held in Sydney in March 1997.[63]

Then it was a surprise to experience intense opposition to the implant from the Signing Deaf Community for its use in children born deaf or deafened before developing language (pre-linguistically deaf) or even going deaf after developing language (post-linguistically deaf). This was in part due to its effect in reducing the numbers of children in the tightly-knit Deaf Community. They could now leave, with the ability to communicate with their hearing peers. It took time for parents to become aware of the good results from Melbourne and other centres. The criticisms have been compared to the Luddite protests in England in the 19th century when technology was replacing established practices.

## Royalties

In 1987, there was much discussion with many lawyers acting for the parties before a licensing agreement was reached about the proportion of royalties that would go to the university and the Commonwealth. The verdict was: the university and the Commonwealth would share equally. I did not realise the long-term implications of this decision until our implant became successful and generated royalties, when we needed all the funding possible to make further advances to keep the implant ahead of the competition.

On 23 September 1987 the first royalties came from the sales of Cochlear Ltd's Implantable Hearing Prosthesis Unit (IHPS) for the calendar years 1985 and 1986 (see the royalties file in the Graeme Clark Collection at the NLA). As Chairman of the Department and leader of the cochlear implant team, I was given the responsibility by the university patents committee of recommending the distribution of the royalties to the inventors and the use of the department's share.

Being one of the main inventors, I asked Dr Field Rickards, a senior lecturer in Audiology, if he would chair the meetings and so avoid a conflict of interest. I held the meeting on 8 October 1987 in the UMDOL with Dr Y. C. Tong, Mr J. F. Patrick and Dr P. M. Seligman. When confidential votes were taken, the key inventors on the basis of patents lodged were Jo Tong, Jim Patrick, Peter Seligman, Bruce Millar, Ray Black and myself. We also decided there were other people who had contributed to the success of the implant and they should receive a smaller percentage of any royalties. Later, after further advances, we considered second round inventors. Each invention in Schedule A was rated according to its use in the commercial bionic ear. They were improvements in prostheses (9%), electrode arrays (11%), speech processors (77%) and connectors (3%). A second meeting chaired by Field Rickards was held on 20 November 1987.

While the Commonwealth was stressing that research should lead to commercial return, it did not make much sense to me that they should penalise one of the few projects that had been successful by taking half the royalties. However, Senator John Button, Minister for Industry, did manage to obtain $500,000 for the development of the electro-tactile device, the "Tickle Talker," though this was later not commercialised. It continued this way till the mid-to-late 1990s when the original patents expired.

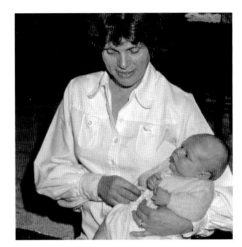

Margaret and Jonathan Clark in 1979.

## Family experiences

While all these activities were happening, it was a joy to bring up five children, encourage them in their studies and participate in a range of activities, whether it was learning to swim, bushwalking, canoeing down the white water rapids in the Yarra River at the front of our house, skiing in the Victorian Alps or boogie board riding the waves at Kiama. We could pursue these activities with zest as a relief from stress involved in developing the bionic ear.

# CHAPTER FOURTEEN

# Further advances in speech coding

Our promising results on adults who had hearing before going deaf became the stimulus for further research to do even better. Funding was required to make these advances.

## Funding the advances in speech coding

When Rod, and later George Watson and others, could understand speech, and Cochlear Ltd had developed their first device industrially, some said, "Job finished, so why do you need more funds?" I had to make it clear I would not stop doing research until most severely/profoundly deaf people could hear almost normally. We had a team of very able scientists, clinicians and support staff to improve our cochlear implant and answer the many questions that still remained, but it appeared I would have meagre research funds to make the essential advances needed to keep the industrial development ahead of the competition. I was grateful for continued assistance through fundraising from the DF Victoria, LCI, the UoM/BEI and many other generous donors. But to provide sustained support for top level scientists, I would have to rely on competitive grants from the NHMRC in the first instance, then the US NIH and next the Australian Research Council (ARC) Centres of Excellence program and the Cooperative Research Centres.

**Peter Stewart, the first bilateral multi-channel cochlear implantee operated on by Brian Pyman, Robert Webb and me at the Epworth Hospital, Melbourne on 18 July 1989.**

After our breakthrough with Rod Saunders, I reapplied to the NHMRC, which had previously denied my requests. But in 1979, when I met the committee after all the publicity about our achievement, they were all smiles and came to the party with funding. That meant I could keep Jo Tong and Ray Black to continue our research at a critical time in making the transition to industry.

The immediate need was to discover how to improve the speech code, learn more about the best methods of inserting the electrode bundles into the inner ear, and discover the answers to many other questions.

## The first public hospital cochlear implant clinic in the world

To maintain an effective clinical research program, I needed to link it to the RVEEH. It was fortunate that in 1985 I was being consulted by the Victorian Minister for Health, Mr Tom Roper, and able to tell him how a clinic in a public hospital would help deaf people in Victoria. He agreed to the proposal and the link was soon established. The clinic has helped deliver quality services to all in the state of Victoria as well as Tasmania. Furthermore, as the number of patients increased, Cochlear Ltd established an innovative way of providing ongoing services through allied Cochlear Care Centres centrally and at nodes around the metropolis.

## Research programs

### The first improvement in speech coding

The place-coding strategy, involving addition of F1 to F2 using Cochlear Ltd's new WSP-III speech processor, led to a further improvement in speech understanding. We selected the lowest F1 frequency band as well as the higher F2 and stimulated two electrodes at the same time. This was underpinned by our psychophysical studies which had shown when two electrodes were stimulated, two sensations could be detected in the one sound, as would be expected for the two formants of vowels. In other words, the brain creates a single conscious experience from more than one site of neural excitation.

To further encourage Cochlear Ltd to develop this first and second formant (F0/F1/F2/A0) code, I suggested to newly-appointed staff member Peter Blamey that we create a model of what electrical stimulation sounded like in normal hearing subjects, and then create an acoustic F0/F1/F2/A0 code.[64] This was successfully trialled by us, and so Cochlear Ltd reconfigured the implant and speech processor, and then oversaw an international clinical study in Australia, the USA, Canada, West Germany, Switzerland, Norway and Japan, for FDA approval in the USA.

We showed the addition of F1 as a place code in FO/F1/F2/AO gave better results than our first FO/F2/AO code.

The new FO/F1/F2/AO code implemented by Cochlear Ltd was evaluated for nine patients at the UoM's clinic after three months, and compared with the old FO/F2/AO code for 13 patients with the same background.[65] For electrical stimulation alone, the CID open-set sentence scores were 14% for FO/F2/AO and 35% for FO/F1/F2/AO, and the monosyllabic word scores were 5% for FO/F2/AO and 12% for FO/F1/F2/AO. In making comparisons, it is always important to define not only the speech code but also the processor used to present the code. The FO/F1/F2/AO code and an improved speech processor, WSP-III, were approved by the FDA in May 1986 for use in post-linguistically deaf adults.

## The second improvement in speech coding: The Multipeak speech code

Not wanting us to fall behind in what had now become a race to achieve the best results, I had to provide more space and facilities for the ARC Centre of Excellence, the Human Communication Research Centre (HCRC) awarded to UMDOL. I aimed to provide more high frequency information in the F3 region. But rather than selecting a peak of energy in the high F3 region, audiologist Richard Dowell and engineer Peter Seligman proposed extracting the energy of the high frequencies from three frequency bands (2,000 to 2,800 Hz, 2,800 to 4,000 Hz, and >4,000 Hz). It was a composite scheme between formant extraction and fixed filters and was referred to as the Multipeak strategy (MSP). When compared with the FO/F1/F2/AO code and WSP-III wearable speech processor there was a 10% increase in vowels and 31% increase for consonants leading to an increase in open-set monosyllabic word scores from 14% to 29%.[66] The Multipeak-MSP code was approved by the US FDA for use in post-linguistically deaf adults on 11 October 1989.

When the Symbion/Ineraid system was compared with our Multipeak-MSP code instead of the earlier FO/F1/F2/AO code there was a big difference in the results. There was a 75% score for the Multipeak-MSP strategy and only a 42% score for the Symbion/Ineraid system.[67] Both codes presented information along the same number of channels, and although the Ineraid did not have a voicing decision, the better results with Multipeak-MSP were not likely due to that alone, but also the spatial pattern of formants and filter outputs over a greater range of frequencies in the cochlea.

So although the loss of inner ear function had created a "bottleneck" for transmitting speech sounds to the brain we were able to send the essential formant representation through the "bottleneck." It was still not normal hearing and the speech pattern was disrupted if there was competing noise, but speech perception had become very good.

## The third improvement in speech coding: Maximal filter bank outputs

We still needed to discover better methods of coding the rapid changes in formant frequencies, especially for better recognition of consonants and for plosives such as "b," "d" and "g." The recognition of the plosives depends especially on the direction of the F2 frequency and its rate of rise or fall, as well as the frequency of the burst of noise that precedes it. We aimed to achieve this by subdividing large formant frequency groups into smaller, more manageable ones.

I was impressed the US NIH were prepared to help fund this new research direction to achieve better results by selecting the maximal outputs of a bank of frequency filters. Between 1985 to 1991 we began by comparing our Multipeak-MSP system with a new code that selected the four highest outputs from a bank of 22 frequency filters. The NIH speech processing reports[68] show the progress we had made. The mean results for vowels were: Multipeak-MSP, 76% and selected 4-filter spectral maxima DSP, 84%; and the mean results for consonants were: Multipeak-MSP, 66% and selected 4-filter maxima DSP, 81%. This strategy indicated the importance of selecting spectral energy from fixed filters for 22 electrodes.

To further improve our strategy, Hugh McDermott recommended we present six of the greatest outputs from a series of 16 frequency filters to pass through the electro-neural "bottleneck."[69] Again, there was an improvement in speech perception. This was referred to as Spectral Maxima Sound coding.

A version that extracted the maximal outputs from 20 rather than 16 filters was developed industrially by Cochlear Ltd and named SPEAK Spectra-22. A multi-centre comparison of the

208

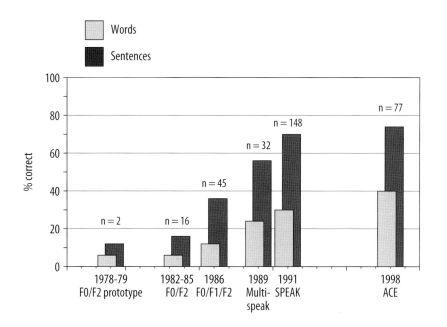

Open-set word (light grey) and in-sentence word (dark grey) results for electrical stimulation alone using second formant (FO/F2/AO), first and second formant (FO/F1/F2/AO), Multipeak, SPEAK and Advanced Combination Encoder (ACE) speech codes.

SPEAK Spectra-22 and Multipeak-MSP strategies was next undertaken on 63 post-linguistically deaf adults at eight centres in Australia, North America and the UK.[70] The mean scores for open sets of words in sentences was 76% for SPEAK Spectra-22 and 67% for Multipeak-MSP.

SPEAK Spectra-22 was approved by the FDA for post-linguistically deaf adults on 30 March 1994. By way of comparison with the Clarion system developed by Advanced Bionics, the Continuous Interleaved Sampler[71] (CIS) gave a mean open-set CID sentence score of 60% for 64 patients at the same six months' post-operative period. The CIS strategy used six filters and stimulated at 800 pulses/s. The better scores with the SPEAK Spectra-22 indicated this was due to a better spatial representation of the important frequencies, particularly for consonants.

The open-set word scores for electrical stimulation alone with the SPEAK strategy varied, but a majority were at levels where useful conversations could be made without the need to lipread.

## The fourth improvement in speech coding:
## The Advanced Combination Encoder (ACE)

Not satisfied until we achieved near-normal speech perception, we presented the Spectral Maxima Sound patterns at higher rates. This strategy developed by Cochlear Ltd became known as the Advanced Combination Encoder (ACE). The ACE strategy was evaluated on 62 post-linguistically deaf adults who were users of SPEAK at 21 centres in the USA. The rate and number of channels were optimised for ACE and compared with CIS. The independent, well-controlled studies showed that ACE was significantly better than SPEAK or CIS. Thus, there has been a steady improvement in our speech coding since 1978 as successive strategies have transmitted more important information.

## Implants for ears with residual hearing:
## Hybrid cochlear implant

We also had to consider how to combine acoustic and electrical information in people with some useful residual hearing. The functioning inner ear was considered to be inviolable and not to be operated on, but I found with Ray Black and others that an electrode inserted through the round window of the experimental animal with care resulted in no significant loss of hearing at any frequencies.[72] Furthermore, we discovered inner ear auditory cells were preserved in the cat and monkey cochleae implanted with and without electrical stimulation, unless there was infection or trauma to the basilar membrane and the spiral lamina.[73] The biological aspects are discussed in more detail in the chapter "Neurobiology" in my textbook.

Patients with an electrode stimulating the high frequency region were able to combine the sensations with acoustic information from a hearing aid exciting the lower frequency region. Note, in the following diagrams, electrical stimulation of the inner ear for hearing losses above 1,000 Hz to 3,000 Hz is needed, provided there is little damage to the low frequency region.

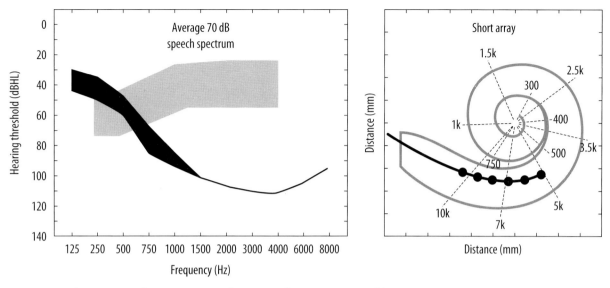

**LEFT: Audiogram of average 70-dB speech spectrum of hearing thresholds plotted against frequency for patients suitable for a hybrid implant. RIGHT: Short electrode array to stimulate high frequency regions.[74]**

## Bilateral cochlear implants

One very pressing need for patients with a cochlear implant is to hear conversation in the presence of background noise. In quiet, for electrical stimulation alone, the comprehension level is 80%, compared to 100% for normal hearing. But when the noise gets louder and the signal-to-noise ratio (SNR) reaches 10 dB, comprehension falls to 60% with the implant but stays close to 100% for normal ears. When the signal and noise levels are the same, i.e. a zero SNR, the speech comprehension with an implant falls dramatically to below 10%, while the normal ear is surprisingly good, at 80%.

To achieve these results, I was keen to provide implants in each ear—that is, binaural hearing. Hence, Brian Pyman and I carried out the first bilateral multi-channel implant on 18 July 1989 on Peter Stewart, a sports journalist from Bendigo.

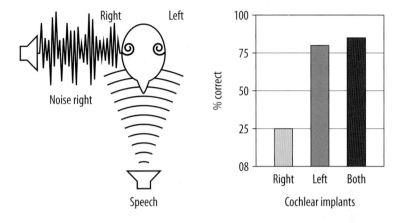

**Speech perception in noise for bilateral implants in my first patient.**

As with the first monaural patients in 1978 and 1979, I aimed with the bilateral patients to study one and then two intensively and did so with Richard van Hoesel and Jo Tong through our ARC Centre of Excellence, the Human Communication Research Centre (HCRC). The speech code for each implant was F0/F1/F2/A0 with the Multipeak-MSP processor. The competing noise was multi-speaker babble, and responses were recorded when the signals were presented with bilateral but independent processors. This determined the benefits in a real-life situation (a room full of noise) where the head shadow had to be taken into consideration. The binaural results for independent processors in quiet were on average 10% better than the best monaural side. At a 5-dB SNR they were almost 50% better.[75] A similar improvement in noise was seen for the Spectral Maxima Sound Processor and SPEAK strategies. Similar results were found for a second patient Steve Pleiter. The better results were in part due to binaural release from masking. This occurs when there is a correlation between the neural responses to the signals from each side but not to the noise. The correlation is due to the speech signals from each side being time-locked and in phase, while noise is more random.

Studies showed the effect of the head blocking, or masking, noise from the opposite side. In other words, if you are listening to speech in the left ear it will be clearer if the noise comes from the right. If the speech is from the front, it arrives at both ears at the same intensity level. If we assume that both ears have equal hearing, we can see that with noise to the right ear there is a marked loss of speech perception in the right ear but good hearing in the left ear. There is only a small improvement when both implants are switched on.

In our next study the subject's hearing in each ear was not equally good, and so the speech perception was better in one ear than the other. In this case, with a bilateral implant there was an advantage when the noise was on the side of the better ear and the signal on the worse side. It suggests that the side attended to is the one with the better SNR even if the performance is poorer.

## Bimodal cochlear implants

Another way of improving speech perception, especially in noise, is bimodal speech processing using electrical stimulation with an implant in one ear and acoustic stimulation with a hearing aid in

**Malcolm Matheson, the first adult to have a bimodal cochlear implant (1990–1991).**

the other ear. This research has become a necessity, as the results obtained with implants have become on average better than for people with severe/profound losses using a hearing aid. These people should have a significant improvement if the signals are combined.

In 1988 and 1989, we commenced research for the first time on bimodal speech coding. The research, in conjunction with Cochlear Ltd, developed a processor that allowed different strategies to be developed and incorporated as a silicon chip. The first patient, Malcolm Matheson had the operation in 1990. The results were the first to be reported for a bimodal cochlear implant.[76]

The results from a study on adults showed that perception was better for bimodal than monaural speech processing in the presence of competing noise. This could have been due to the head shadow effect or binaural release from masking.

In summary, the findings showed the value of implanting an ear opposite to the one with useful hearing. The main difference between monaural and binaural hearing was a better result for bimodal coding in the presence of noise, where it was significantly better. Further information is available from the 4th to 10th annual reports of the Australian Bionic Ear and Hearing Institute from 1989 to 1996. These are housed in the Graeme Clark Collection at the NLA.

## What factors predict favourable outcomes?

As there were variations in results, it was of interest to know what factors led to best outcomes. A thorough medical examination is a necessity to determine the cause of the hearing loss and whether there are factors that mitigate against surgery, such as an untreated middle ear infection. A complete audiological investigation is also required, and that is now accompanied by steady state-evoked response audiometry in children. The recording of cochlear microphonics and ABR tests for neuropathy are important, as are CT, x-ray scans and/or MRI. Electrical stimulation of the auditory nerve through the middle ear was a prerequisite.

Now with a very significant improvement in the results of the Cochlear Ltd implant, the clinical procedures have been modified. But patients rightly want to know the probability of success, as might be expected of any surgical or medical procedure. A detailed analysis of results in the 1980s and 1990s has shown that for post-linguistically deaf people the duration of the deafness is a key factor, as is the speech coding strategy and the number of electrodes inserted into the cochlea. There are still many elderly people who stand to benefit and should be reminded that age is not a deterrent. We have successfully implanted people in their 90s. Similar outcome predictors exist for pre-linguistically deaf people, but the age of implantation is crucial.

## Funding the research

The improvements in speech coding were made possible through funding I received in 1988 for the award of the HCRC as a Centre of Excellence from the ARC, the grant most sought-after by biological scientists. This was in addition to the NHMRC program grant in 1984, specifically for medical research. These were for nine years so they gave some security. They gave us freedom to explore ideas that I believed were new, exciting and important. In fact, the research in both centres was some of the most productive I had the privilege of leading. There was also a need for research of benefit to industry through a government Cooperative Research Centres scheme. I found myself Director of three Australian centres, and Chief Investigator for two US NIH grants, and a grant from the DF. It got to the stage where, when cochlear implant surgery was in progress, I had a closed-circuit television to my office so I could still supervise and comment on insertions of the electrode arrays by the senior surgeons when I was working with my wonderful personal assistants, Joan Maher and Margaret Gilmour. Looking back, I realise it was an incredibly busy time from 1985 to 1995 when I was 50 to 60 years of age—just at the right time of my life.

# CHAPTER FIFTEEN

# Speech perception and spoken language in children with a cochlear implant

My greatest passion, one that had driven me through many years of struggle, was the desire to give hearing, and especially speech perception and spoken language, to deaf children. I remember the concern I felt in the 1950s when, as a medical student, I travelled by train from Summer Hill to MacDonald Town station, and walked across City Road just near the Deaf, Dumb and Blind Institute in Darlington on my way to UoS. At recess, the children were either very quiet or made strange-sounding noises.

When I was appointed to the Alfred Hospital, Melbourne in 1964, I would see children from the Victorian School for Deaf Children and as *pro bono* work, repair perforations in their eardrums to help manage their deafness. Although they were enjoying themselves, it was obvious how difficult it was for them to communicate.

Then, in 1967 when I returned to Sydney to do electrophysiological research, I would again enter the university by the same route as I had taken as a medical student. The deaf school, since acquired by the UoS, reminded me of my desire to help deaf children.

After I was appointed to the Chair in Otolaryngology in Melbourne in late 1969, I realised the importance of focussing my efforts on multi-channel electrical stimulation of the auditory brain for the benefit of severely/profoundly deaf children. The public exposure of my research through the telethons from 1973 meant some congenitally deaf people wanted to see me, not being satisfied with their communication skills using sign language. Moreover, I knew (from other people's work with hearing aids) how

**Bryn (aged 5 years) and Scott (aged 10 years) were among the first children to receive a cochlear implant.**

important it was to provide hearing at an early age for best speech perception and spoken language. This work clearly revealed that the more severe the deafness and the older the child when hearing was restored, the worse their speech and communication skills.

## Preliminary perceptual studies

To decide at what age a deaf child could be implanted, I had regular discussions with Dan Ling, renowned Canadian deaf educationist who visited in the early 1980s with his partner Gaye Musgrave. I well remember a discussion in my office in 1984 when Dan agreed it would only be appropriate to implant a child after they reached the age of four, as tests at that time were not reliable before that. We would have to show that the child did not have useful low frequency hearing before any surgery, because it could be lost following an implant.

However, in the early 1980s my research with Field Rickards, then Lecturer in Audiology in the UMDOL, demonstrated that we could diagnose a hearing loss in all frequencies at birth by recording brain electric potentials from modulating the amplitude of sounds. We carried this out with a special analysis (a Fourier analysis) of the waveforms. After we were sure the test was reliable, the way was opened to operate on deaf infants of six months of age and give them a greater chance of having near-normal speech and language.

But to commence the research and gather preliminary data ethically, I selected two young adults in their early 20s, who could responsibly make their own decisions after careful explanation of the risks and benefits. The two pre-linguistically deaf young adults were Greg (aged 24 years, deafened early in life) and Beverly (aged 23 years, born deaf). Both had learned to communicate with Australian Sign Language (Auslan). I led the surgery on Greg in September in 1983 and Beverly in November 1983.

Post-operatively, these two people could not detect simple electrical stimuli as well as those who had hearing before going deaf. They had more difficulty with both rate of stimulation and identifying the electrode place.[77] These difficulties were consistent with their poor speech recognition. The results convinced me that I should seek out younger people, and especially those who had been educated to use residual hearing. They also needed to have better "top-down" processing of the new sounds from electrical stimuli. "Top-down" processing refers to higher cortical functioning such as reasoning and memory, as distinct from "bottom-up" processing, where the initial coding of information occurs.

The perceptual tests emphasised that place pitch coding was most important for speech perception, but it needed to be learned early in life. They also suggested that the different grammar used with Auslan could have been a factor in their poorer results. Whatever speech code was used it had to be presented at a young age while the brain was still plastic.

To also understand what educational (habilitation) challenges we would face, I carried out studies with colleagues Peter Busby and Jo Tong on four adolescent pre-linguistically deaf children using hearing aids. This helped identify the perceptually important parameters in speech when presented visually, as audition, or in combination. The important acoustic parameters being used were F1 and F2 frequencies and vowel length.[78]

We planned to engage in research on implanted children when the program to help adults deafened later in life was well under way. I did not believe it was justified for us to gain experience on children first, as we had discovered there was a learning period in managing the surgery. It was also not clear how best to develop speech perception and spoken language. Furthermore, we had to be as sure as possible the children in future years would not regret the decision that their parents had made if there were unexpected problems later. I also assumed the development of language in children would probably require a different approach from the one we had used for restoring speech perception and hearing for adults who had hearing and language before they went deaf. For that reason, I engaged two speech pathologists Shani Dettman and Elizabeth Barker. I also worked closely with an audiologist and speech pathologist, Dianne Mecklenberg, who had transferred from the USA, and Terry Nienhuys, the first senior academic in the UoM Education Department.[79] As a result, we produced a rehabilitation/habilitation program for children which became a model for Dianne to adapt for the USA at a later stage.

At first, the children were taught in the traditional way of speech pathologists and educators to get pronunciation correct, word by word. Then I realised their speech was sounding unnatural, like "deaf speak"—not the outcome I was seeking. It was not till I advised speaking to them normally to get the prosody right that we made real progress with their speech.

## How to prevent the risk of meningitis?

Before operating on young children, I used experimental animals, as I had done from the beginning for adults, to ensure an implant would be biologically safe. There were specific questions, such as the effect of head growth and a maturing nervous system. Young children are prone to middle ear disease that could lead to inner ear infection and meningitis, and this requires attention in order to be avoided.[80]

The award of a seven-year contract by the US NIH helped us to find safe methods.[81] For example, we first glued matted polyester fibres to the electrode bundle where it entered the inner ear at the round window, aiming for it to be infiltrated with fibrous tissue to increase the path length and stop bacteria entering the inner ear. Our research showed the foreign material could provide a home for the infection and prevent the body's cells attacking the infective organisms. For that reason, I also set out to graft tissue from the animal's own body (autograft of muscle or fibrous tissue) around the electrode entry point to see if that would provide an effective seal. I used three types of bacteria, as their invasive properties and prevalence in the upper respiratory tract are different: staphylococcus aureus, β haemolytic streptococcus type A, and pneumococcus. The results showed that a graft of tissue from the animal's own body at the electrode entry point was the best approach, because a sheath formed around the electrode and acted as a barrier to the entry of infection. The sheath adhered closely to the electrode and through its blood supply brought cells to fight any bacteria.

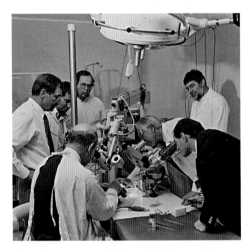

**Our team studying the insertion of an electrode with spacer into human temporal bone.**

Another team of bioengineers overseas overlooked these issues and developed an electrode bundle with two components and a space between

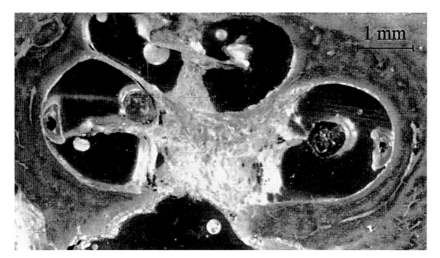

A cross section of the
human cochlea showing
the damage created
by an electrode with
spacer and also the
space between the two.

them that allowed the entry of infection from the middle to the inner ear with resultant mening-itis.[82] Several children actually died.[83] The electrode array had a second member that forced it to hug the centre of the cochlear spiral to lie close to the auditory nerves. This created an open space between the two components, letting bacteria enter from a middle ear infection. This showed, yet again, how important it is to have bioengineers working closely with surgeons with a science background. We had studied this design in the laboratory and also found that it damaged the cochlea.

It was unsurprising then that in September 2002 at the 7th International Cochlear Implant Conference in Manchester, the Signing Deaf Community came out in force, with black coffins. There was a demonstration and we were all locked in the auditorium for our safety. One protester had even climbed to the roof to display a banner saying: "Better Deaf than Dead."

In a press release and public addresses, I had to make it clear that we had done studies over many years to ensure the safety of implanting young children. As a result, there was a dramatic restoration of Cochlear Ltd's share price, helped also by my being able to say I had no shares in the company. Then, working closely with Professor Noel Cohen from New York and the FDA, I helped establish the correct protocols for safe surgery.[84]

# Council backs down on street sex sites

**Kerrah Tomazin**

The Port Phillip Council is expected to drop a controversial proposal to let transsexual prostitutes work in a "tolerance zone" outside the St Kilda Town Hall.

The council may also abandon a proposal to create a tolerance area for male street sex workers around Chaucer Street and Shakespeare Grove. Cavell Street, behind Luna Park, has instead been chosen as the proposed zone for male prostitutes.

Residents earlier this week criticised the council's proposed sites, saying some could affect safety, traffic and trade.

Under the changes, transsexual sex workers would be able to solicit at night at a car park behind the Acland Street shopping strip. This area was part of the original short-list.

A proposal to let female prostitutes trade along a 24-hour zone on St Kilda Road, between Inkerman and Barkly Streets, remains on the council's shortlist, as does the proposed female zone around Junction Oval, near Fitzroy Street and Lakeside Drive.

But the Lakeside Drive side of the oval, near the St Kilda Park Primary School, would be able to operate only at night.

Port Phillip chief executive David Spokes said the town hall was dropped from the list because it was felt that one zone was adequate for transsexual sex workers.

Residents welcomed the changes. Carlisle Street resident Peter Jordan, who lives opposite the town hall, said he was relieved. Chaucer Street resident Judy-Ann Steed said the council had shown common sense by chopping the Chaucer street zone, but said there were still problems with other proposed sites.

The council will consider the revised list on Monday before referring the matter to an independent panel.

## COCHLEAR IMPLANTS

# Father of bionic ear lashes out at deadly design

**David Wroe, Ian Porter**

The Australian inventor of the bionic ear yesterday defended the technology, blaming a badly designed United States device for the deaths of nine wearers from meningitis.

Professor Graeme Clark's words came too late for the Australian maker of bionic ears, Cochlear Ltd, whose sharemarket value was stripped by $200 million as the safety fears spread.

Professor Clark, who pioneered cochlear implant technology in the 1970s, said the deaths — believed to be five in Europe and four in the US — could all be attributed to the US design fault, which had created a home for bacterial "slime" in the wearer's ear.

The Clarion implant, made by Advanced Bionics Corporation, is not used in this

> **The company concerned . . . has in fact made a design change that is dangerous.**
> GRAEME CLARK

country. Professor Clark emphasised Cochlear Ltd used a safe design and the 2000 Australians who had been implanted were not at risk of meningitis.

Cochlear shares fell almost 20 per cent before closing at $29.80. The company, which grew from the old Pacific Dunlop group in 1995, finished its first day of trade at $2.85. Last November it reached a peak of $52.40.

Professor Clark lashed out at the US company, saying its engineers had apparently not consulted medical experts when designing the device in two pieces, creating a "dead space" for bacteria to thrive in.

"It just amazes me. We've known in medicine and biology for years that dead spaces are bad news," Professor Clark said. "The company concerned with the . . . nine deaths has in fact made a design change that is dangerous."

The deaths from meningitis — an inflammation of the mem-

branes covering the brain and spinal cord usually caused by bacterial infection — had occurred over the past three or four years, he said.

The US Food and Drug Administration announced on Thursday it had "become aware of a possible association between cochlear implants and the occurence of bacterial meningitis".

It said there had been nine deaths and at least 25 cases worldwide among adults and children ranging in age from 21 months to 63 years. More than 60,000 people worldwide have had implants.

Professor Clark — who has no financial interest in the Australian company Cochlear — said he was disappointed the FDA did not specify that the deaths were linked only to the Clarion implant.

"To be tarnished by a company that has actually designed something incorrectly is very disappointing," he said.

He said Cochlear's device, called Nucleus, was the only implant used in Australia and had not been linked to any cases of meningitis in Australia.

Cochlear's company secretary, Neville Mitchell, said there had been some cases of meningitis among implant recipients overseas, but that the rate of infection was about the same as in the general population. There had been no meningitis deaths from among its 38,500 recipients anywhere in the world, he said.

The Clarion design has been withdrawn in Germany, France and Spain. The US is considering withdrawing approval.

The FDA statement emphasised that because meningitis had taken up to five years to develop in some victims, there were likely to be more cases.

Professor Clark said the dead space in the Clarion implant provided a path for the bacteria from the middle to the inner ear and made the bacteria "aggro".

He believed the company had changed the design to make the implant more efficient by getting it closer to the inner ear.

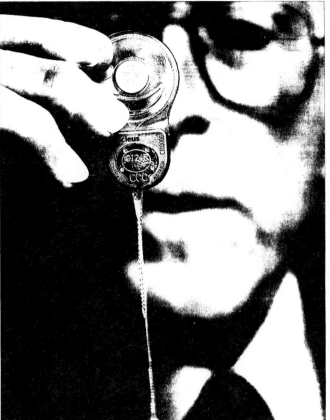

Professor Graeme Clark, inventor of the cochlear implant, at his press conference yesterday.
PICTURE: JOHN WOUDSTRA

# Plan to expand specialist schools

**Ewin Hannan**
State Editor

State secondary school students could travel to different schools for classes in art and design, information technology, music, languages, sport and science, under State Government plans to have networks of schools offer different specialist subjects.

Education Minister Lynne Kosky said yesterday the government wanted "to push the boundaries across every area of the curriculum" and allow students to leave their own school to access specialist subjects at neighbouring schools.

Under the plan, secondary schools would form "clusters" with neighbouring schools and strike agreements to teach different specialist subjects.

"Many schools are already specialising in art and design, in IT and in music," Ms Kosky

thing. "Schools can't be excellent at everything, but they should excel in something," she said. "The challenge is to share that so that students have broader offerings. Many schools are already doing this. The government's challenge is to assist all schools to excel."

Ms Kosky said the approach should not be confused with establishing specialist schools, or selective entry to schools.

She said the government did not want schools to compete but to cooperate. Schools that did not offer specialist subjects or form clusters would not suffer reduced access to resources.

While schools would determine the most appropriate model, options included bussing students to nearby schools and specialist teachers potentially working several hours at a different school. Ms Kosky said rural areas, where students had longer distances to travel between schools could utilise

offer all students a broad curriculum choice and the chance to excel," she said.

"We want them to be excited about learning and for each student to make real achievements.

"This means we need to push the boundaries across every area of the curriculum, and we need our schools to work together — so so many of them are already — to offer broad choices as well as having access to a range of specialist choices within geographic areas."

Resourcing and timetabling issues were yet to be worked out. The Australian Education Union's state president, Mary Bluett, said union members were interesting in pursuing the policy.

Ms Bluett said the union was also finalising a policy platform to put to the major political parties in the lead-up to the state election. The union would

A review of the data as of July 2002 indicated that most did not have device-related meningitis. However, as children with a cochlear malformation have a higher risk, they should be vaccinated against meningitis. The US Advisory Committee on Immunization Practices has recommended that all candidates for cochlear implants should be immunised prior to surgery.

## Non-invasive tactile stimulators

In 1984 and 1985, as I had no evidence yet that electrical stimulation of the auditory brain would give adequate speech understanding in children, I considered it advisable to first see whether a non-invasive procedure using patterns of skin stimulation would be effective. Could patterns of stimulation of one sense, such as touch, be given meaning in another modality for speech and language? There had been evidence that when a visual field had been presented to the back of a subject, it became so real they ducked when the pattern appeared to come closer. Furthermore, in experimental animal studies, if the auditory input to the cells in the brain was cancelled, the visual input to the auditory region increased. Could a similar change occur with tactile stimulation and lead to good speech understanding?

But there were problems in delivering the tactile stimuli, as vibrators were large and used a lot of power, while electrical stimulation of the skin using smaller electrodes stimulated pain fibres. I had a grant from philanthropist Ian Sheddon to explore and improve on these alternatives. On the last day, with negative results and money running out, I offered my arm for the study and was surprised that when a sensory nerve bundle in the arm (the medial cutaneous nerve of the forearm) was stimulated electrically, the sensation was acceptable. I concluded that the ideal solution was to present the speech frequencies by electrical stimulation of the digital nerves running down either side of the fingers, each representing a different speech frequency on a place-coding basis. This became our clinical trial device dubbed the "Tickle Talker." I tried it first on our two-year-old son Jonathan to see if it would be manageable, and also did extensive studies on blood flow to the hands of volunteers to be sure there were no unanticipated long-term ill effects.

Then, Peter Blamey and I looked at how well the brain could embrace tactile patterns as conscious representations of speech.[85] This included an early trial on the second child scheduled

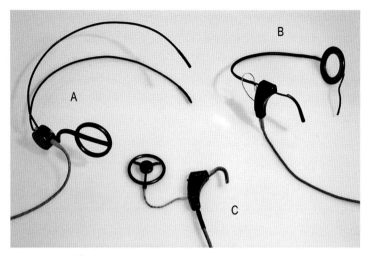

**Headset designs used by Nucleus/Cochlear Ltd.**
**A: Original headset (1982–1985).**
**B: Behind-the-ear headset (1982–1985).**
**C: Coil with central magnet.**

for a cochlear implant (Scott S.). He interpreted the stimuli as speech, but not well enough to forego the trial of electrical stimulation of the auditory brain pathways.

When the electro-tactile strategy was trialled on a cohort of deaf people there were significant increases in speech scores, making it a possible alternative to the cochlear implant for young children.[86] I was torn between the two possibilities. The "Tickle Talker" was highlighted on the television program *Quantum* and its industrial development had support from the federal government and Senator John Button's blessing was revealed in a press report.

## Preparing to do cochlear implants on children

By 1985, I was still not sure if a multi-channel cochlear implant or "Tickle Talker" was the better option for severely/profoundly deaf children. Intuitively, I held the view that the auditory pathways were formed in a way that they could handle the complex patterns of speech when coded as electrical stimuli, but of course was unaware of the spectacular results we would later achieve by implanting children at a very young age.

Finally, to make a bet both ways, I decided we should not only see how well skin stimulation could convey speech but at the same time design the implant to use with children. Any design improvements for children would also be of benefit to adults.

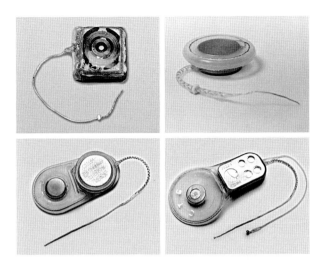

**Development of the Nucleus receiver-stimulator packages. Top left: the University of Melbourne prototype (1979). Top right: Nucleus clinical trial implant (1982). Bottom left: Nucleus CI22 Mini (1985). Bottom right: Nucleus CI24 (1990s).**

One key change was to redesign the headset so that the transmitting and receiving coils were easily aligned. The initial head clasps were cumbersome, and children would readily dislodge them. The solution was to insert rare earth magnets in the centre of the inside and outside coils, as suggested by Ken Dormer from Ohio, who got the idea from his fridge magnets.[87]

The Nucleus implantable receiver-stimulator had the coil and magnet at the back, so that it would be thinner for children's skulls. When FDA approval for our multi-channel implant for post-linguistically deaf adults was imminent in 1985, I felt reassured and was prepared to commence our program on children using the Nucleus 22 Mini.

## Undertaking the first cochlear implant on children with some hearing

There was still a strong undercurrent of scepticism even among my auditory/oral supporters. Being in charge of the whole cochlear implant research and clinical program, I could not shelve responsibility for any mishaps. So, with capable assistance from Robert Webb, I led the surgery on 8 January 1985 on the first child, Peter S., after an unsuccessful trial with the tactile "Tickle Talker."

Peter S., aged 14, was privately referred by his parents, who did not want him to miss the critical period. They had to pay $10,000 for the implant, as we had no government funding. Peter made steady progress, but I was disappointed that he did not have useful speech understanding

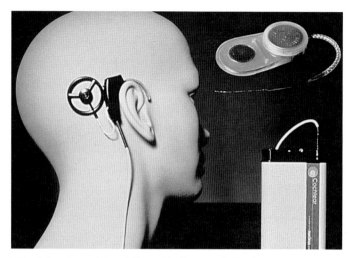

**The Nucleus/Cochlear Ltd CI22 Mini cochlear implant with magnet in the centre of the transmitting and receiving coils and a pocket-sized speech processor (1985).**

with electrical stimulation alone.

Pressing on towards the goal of operating on younger children, we had 10-year-old Scott, whose parents were keen for him to hear. During the early part of 1985, he had training with the "Tickle Talker" with sub-optimal results, and so on 20 August Rob Webb and I performed his cochlear implant operation, which went without incident.

Our first international Cochlear Implant Symposium and Workshop in 1985 (only the second after Paris in 1984) was scheduled for shortly after Scott's surgery between 27 and 31 August. A few visitors remained for his "switch on," scheduled for two weeks after his operation in early September. I approached the occasion with confidence gained from the early encouraging results from our post-linguistically deaf adults. However, it was embarrassing that instead of a rapturous expression of joy at hearing, Scott became very distressed. What a public relations failure! It was only after wise counselling by our audiologists that Scott settled down when he accepted the fact that he would have to learn the meaning of new speech sounds. The next day, he returned with a completely different attitude, and training commenced in earnest. Although I did not want to go to the press prematurely, when I saw progress with Scott, I agreed to a television documentary produced by *Quantum* and released in October. This created a storm of protests. I felt it was ironic that I was now confronted by the very people I wanted to give an opportunity to hear. The criticisms affected all members of the team and weighed heavily on us. However, our spirits brightened when Scott showed much

226

better speech perception results than Peter's (31% for a closed set of 12 consonants).[88]

Early in 1986, with eldest daughter Sonya, I travelled as the Australian Vice Chancellor's nominee from all universities to represent medical research in Australia at a Houston festival, which was honouring Australia. Apart from meeting Bobby Alford, Professor of Otolaryngology and Vice President of Baylor Medical College, this gave me an opportunity to visit pioneer audiologist Jim Jerger and Bill House at the House Ear Institute in Los Angeles on the way home. Bill had commenced doing single-channel cochlear implants on children, much to the concern of the general ENT community. Their results were not better than a less invasive tactile aid, although they did give awareness of sound.

Believing that results would be better on even younger children because of brain plasticity, I was pleased to be referred a five-year-old boy (Bryn D.) who was profoundly deaf due to meningitis. His referral came from the sisters at St Mary's School for the Deaf, the only school that had faith in what I was doing to assist deaf children. They were using a form of education (cued speech) that was consistent with the restoration of auditory/oral or auditory verbal communication. It retained the grammar of English as distinct from sign languages of the deaf, in which grammar was very different.

Before the operation, Bryn, like Scott before him, had a trial period with the "Tickle Talker" for electro-tactile stimulation, without much success. Then, after a careful audiological review, Rob Webb and I implanted Bryn on 15 April 1986 at the RVEEH. By April 1986, I had operated on three severely/profoundly deaf children at the RVEEH.

This was the first time the Cochlear Ltd multi-channel prosthesis had been implanted in young deaf children, and it received considerable press coverage.

The F0/F1/F2/A0 speech code was used for five-year-old Bryn and his initial results were better. Our three children had developed some language in the three years before their operation but were still classified as pre-linguistically deaf.

## The first implant on a child who had no prior hearing

It was still not clear whether the brain was responding to patterns of electrical stimuli that were exciting neural connections prepared through prior exposure to sound, or whether our speech code could initiate speech understanding in children born deaf where the neurons were nascent. As two of our three children were progressing well, I was keen to implant a child profoundly deaf from birth. The most deserving one in our clinic was 14-year-old Colleen Tarrant, who not only fitted that category but was going blind. If we did not operate soon, it would be much harder for her to recognise speech without help from lipreading. Her surgery was in April 1987, and before long she was able to understand speech with help from lipreading. Later that year, my surgical mentor and old school friend Barrie Scrivener, together with professorial colleague Bill Gibson from the UoS, operated on a second child, eight-year-old Pia Jeffrey at RPAH. She too was able to understand speech with our implant.

## Clinical trial by Cochlear Ltd for the Food and Drug Administration

The results on two of the first three children in 1985 and 1986 helped Cochlear Ltd obtain US FDA approval at the end of 1986 to commence a clinical trial in the USA, Europe and Australia on deaf children from 2 to 18 years of age. The children used the F0/F1/F2/A0 coding strategy. The first of our multi-channel cochlear implants in the USA was inserted by Dr Bill House in a five-year-old child on 6 February 1987. This was of interest, as Bill had been a strong advocate for his single-channel implant up to this time.

The number of children implanted in Melbourne increased, and in 1989 five (of ages 6 to 14 years) out of a group of nine had substantial open-set speech recognition for electrical stimulation alone when tested with monosyllabic words scored as phonemes (range 30% to 72%), and sentences (range 26% to 74%).[89] These were the first well-substantiated open-set speech perception results on implanted deaf children, and the results I was hoping that we could achieve.

The study for the FDA continued to expand in Australia, the USA and Europe with a total of 32 adolescents (10 to 17 years) and 24 preadolescents (2 to 9 years) having been implanted as of 31 August 1987. I hoped it would show that children, many of whom were deafened before language had developed, would soon be able to hear words as well as those who had hearing and language before going deaf. An early report was made at the Cochlear Implant Symposium in Duren in 1987 on two Australians and two from the USA who had been using the implant for 12 months or more.[90] Three of the four children demonstrated open-set speech recognition post-operatively. The results on our children were first presented to the Annual General Meeting of the Australian Otolaryngological Society in Hobart in 1987. It was a relaxed meeting where colleagues welcomed the findings without the hostile scepticism of the past.

The next two major presentations were to the Royal Swedish Academy of Engineering Science and Nottingham University in the UK in 1999.[91] The results indicated that prior exposure to speech sounds was not essential for forming the right neural connections if an electrical speech code was presented early during the brain's plastic phase of development. My impressions that speech and language were better when we operated at an early age were confirmed by the analyses of Richard Dowell. There was a scatter of results relating to age at implantation. Not all children, when operated on at a young age, did well. But some were outstanding. These results were on children above two years of age as required by the US FDA. It gave me hope that we might see better hearing and language if we operated at a younger age.

In the world trial for the US FDA on children from 2 to 17 years of age, there was a high proportion obtaining open or closed-set speech understanding for electrical stimulation alone. Their performances varied in order of skill from detection, pattern, closed-set, to open-set speech.

During this period, a well-controlled comparative study was undertaken at the CID at St Louis in Missouri, USA for three groups who had hearing aids, tactile stimulation and the Nucleus/Cochlear Ltd implant. But before the completion of the study, it was clear that the children with the multi-channel cochlear implant were performing so much better than the others it would be unethical to continue the study and not give all the children the opportunity to have a multi-channel cochlear implant.

A comprehensive study of speech perception in 46 children under four years compared to 18 post-linguistically deaf adults was undertaken from 1996 to 2002 and I was able to report the results in the Zotterman lecture I gave in 2011 at the Nobel Institute in Stockholm. These showed that children had better results with phonemes and words, while adults were better at recognising sentences, reflecting their greater experience with the language.

# Bionic ear lets boys hear again

By PHILIP McINTOSH

A smaller model of the Australian bionic ear, which has proved successful here and overseas in deaf adults, has been implanted for the first time in children.

Proof of the dramatic progress being made with the device was heard in Melbourne yesterday when its first recipient, a previously deaf 10-year-old, Scott Smith, faced a news conference to answer questions about it.

Scott, who lives in Sunshine, was the first child to have a multi-channel Cochlear implant in an operation at the Royal Victorian Eye and Ear Hospital last August. He was followed by five-year-old Bryn Davies, of Scoresby, who had the operation two months ago.

The head of the Melbourne University bionic ear research team, Professor Graeme Clark, said that before the implant and speech training, Scott's speech intelligibility score was zero. It was now 60 to 70 per cent.

Before the operation, his speech comprehension had also been zero. But yesterday, with some help from speech pathologist Sue Roberts, Scott said: "I can hear things now." These include television, the noise of traffic and the conversation of his school mates.

Scott's week is divided between a special school and a normal school where he is captain of the Australian Rules football team. He said that during games he wore a helmet to protect a radio wave transmitter, worn behind the ear, and its wiring.

His comprehension is aided by lip-reading. His mother, Mrs Betty Smith, has noticed a big change in her son. "The more his speech has improved, the more confident he's become," she said.

Both the child and adult models of the Cochlear prosthesis are made by Cochlear Pty Ltd, one of the Nucleus group of high-technology medical companies based in Sydney. Last year the adult model was approved by the Food and Drug Administration for sale in the United States.

Professor Clark said that clinical trials in the US, Canada and West Germany confirmed its value in helping profoundly or totally deaf adults to understand conversational speech.

Professor Clark said that the child's Cochlear implant was still in the research stage, which would continue for up to two years and involve up to 10 patients.

The Cochlear device is not the only bionic ear available. A single-channel implant, developed by the 3M group and the House Institute in Los Angeles, has also been implanted in hundreds of adults worldwide.

Professor Clark said that studies around the world showed that Cochlear implants using multiple electrodes, and therefore multiple channels or frequencies, produced better speech than those with single electrodes.

A newer, multiple-channel model of the 3M-House device was developed by a research team in Vienna and has been implanted in four patients in Australia.

The first child in Australia to have one of the single-channel units implanted was a six-year-old girl from Gosford in New South Wales in 1984. The girl, Heather Crew, lost all her hearing in 1983 after she contracted meningitis.

Her surgeon, who asked not to be named, said in Sydney last night that a post-lingually deaf person like Heather would be expected to lose her speech. But the Cochlear prosthesis, as an aid to lip-reading, had allowed Heather to stay in a normal school where she was making good progress.

Professor Clark said that hundreds of children in Australia with profound or total deafness could benefit from a successful Cochlear implant.

Initial research for the Melbourne bionic ear program was financed by the National Health and Medical Research Council, the Channel 10 nerve deafness appeal, the Lions Clubs International, and the National Institutes of Health in the US.

The Australian Bionic Ear Institute was incorporated this month to help raise more money for the research.

Pictures: NEALE DUCKWORTH

Now hear this: Bryn Davies, 5, left, and Scott Smith, 10, the first recipients of the new small bionic ear, join Professor Graeme Clark in testifying to its effectiveness.

A bionic ear cradled in Professor Clark's hand.

# Tizzone ch[...] in 1977: p[...]

By FIONA HARARI

SYDNEY. — Gianfranco Tizzone, who was convicted in 1984 for having conspired to murder Donald Mackay, had been considered a "person of interest" as early as 1977 by New South Wales police investigating the murder, but had been given a relatively low priority rating.

A special inquiry into the investigation of Mr Mackay's death was told this on the first day of evidence yesterday.

Tizzone was given the low priority rating despite the fact that he had no alibis on the day Mr Mackay disappeared and on the day, five days earlier, when Mr Mackay was allegedly set up for a meeting at Jerilderie to meet his death. Mr Mackay did not attend the meeting.

In its first day of evidence, the executive chief superintendent of crime in NSW, Mr Frederick Joseph Parrington, told the inquiry that some information about the case had to be obtained through talks between the Victorian and NSW Premiers, after NSW police had failed to secure information from their Victorian counterparts about "someone who could give very good information about what happened to Donald Mackay".

Mr John Nagle, QC, has until 30 November to conclude his inquiry into the police investigation of Mr Mackay's

death, but not the death itself, a[...] consider whether the inquiry, and [...] intendent Parrington's handling [...] were efficient and proper.

Superintendent Parrington, who [...] charge of the Mackay investigati[...] yesterday that Tizzone had been c[...] ered a "person of special interes[...] (police) inquiry and could not b[...] nated". This meant he had not [...] the status of a suspect, but could [...] eliminated from investigation bec[...] could not produce an alibi.

He said NSW police had been [...] October 1977 that a Mr Titsar[...] identified as Tizzone) had bee[...] carrying a pistol at the openin[...] Antonio Sergi's winery at Tarb[...] statement from the Victorian p[...] vealed that Tizzone had no alib[...] July 1977, the day Mr Mackay wa[...] met a Mr Adams at Jerilderie, an[...] 1977, the day Mr Mackay was l[...]

### Special inqui[...]

Superintendent Parrington [...] inquiry: "He (Tizzone) is a p[...] would not allow to drop out [...] investigation."

In later evidence, howeve[...] Tizzone, who was said to be a [...] Robert Trimbole, and who was [...] ed by the Costigan Royal Co[...] could not be located in 1981 w[...]

# Indons stronger than Dibb thinks, says former air chief

By MARK BAKER, diplomatic correspondent

CANBERRA. — A former air force chief has warned that Indonesia has the military capacity to occupy northern Australia with 10,000 troops in less than 48 hours.

Air Marshal David Evans, who retired last year as chief of the air staff, strongly challenged the Dibb Defence Report's assessment that Australia would have 10 years' warning of a substantial assault.

Marshal Evans said he regarded Indonesia as a friendly nation with no intention of attacking Australia. But, he said, defence planners must recognise the reality that Indonesia had the capacity to mount an immediate, large-scale assault on northern Australia

cules) flying backwards and forwards between Timor could fill the place up. They could have 10,000 troops on the ground within 48 hours."

Marshal Evans said that without control of the northern ports and airfields, Australia would be faced with a long and tough land battle to win back control of the north, and would have to call on "the ANZUS partner" — the United States — for help.

Marshal Evans described the defence review by strategic analyst Mr Paul Dibb, released last week, as "an excellent report". But, he said, it had fallen short in providing a proper strategy to recognise the strength of other military forces in the region.

He said there should be a substantial increase in air power based in northern Australia and the nation should buy early-warning aircraft in addition to the Jin-

to build up for an invasion of Papua New Guinea and overfly northern Australia in a provocative way.

"They could have us jumping from one end to the other with our very limited resources and a month would see us absolutely buggered without a shot being fired," he said.

## Cochlear Ltd implant approval by the Food and Drug Administration

It was an exciting announcement on 27 June 1990 that the UoM's multi-channel cochlear implant, developed industrially by Cochlear Ltd, was the first cochlear implant of any type for children to be approved by the US FDA. The speech codes were F0/F1/F2/A0 and Multipeak.

The approval by the FDA was the culmination of all my dreams and hopes for deaf children. This was another Eureka moment!

We now had independent and objective confirmation that the initial impressions from teachers of the deaf who had not seen such progress before, were correct. It helped establish the multi-channel cochlear implant as the first major innovation to help deaf children communicate in the more than 250 years since sign languages of the deaf devised by Abbé de l'Épée. I gained a better understanding of that achievement in helping deaf children communicate when I was in Paris after the 4th European Symposium of Paediatric Cochlear Implantation in the Netherlands (June 1998). I took the opportunity to visit the Paris Deaf School.

Although with the new implant there was now scope for deaf children to enter the world of sound, it has taken many years for most severely/profoundly deaf children to receive the benefits. The many reasons for this include lack of access to well-equipped clinics, a failure to communicate up-to-date findings, entrenched conservatism and the fear of those dependent on sign languages of the deaf of losing their community.

## Preparing to operate on very young children

As very young children in the future were likely to benefit from the cochlear implant, I embarked on surgical anatomical studies to see where best to place the receiver-stimulator to allow for growth and make room for the transmitting and receiving coils to be placed behind their ears. The study was also undertaken to minimise any risk of a middle ear infection, common in this age group and leading to meningitis or the chance of electrical stimulation having an adverse effect on the maturing nervous system. This surgical anatomical research began at the end of 1986 and continued into the early 1990s through a contract with the USA.[92] It was undertaken on 60 specimens and showed the lead wire should have a length of 20 mm to allow for growth

**The opening of the Graeme Clark room in Nottingham, England, 1999.**

between the round window entry to the inner ear and the site of placement, or else the electrode could be pulled out. It also demonstrated that at a point where the short process of the incus rests the lead wire could be fixed with no relative movement between it and the round window. In addition, the studies on infection and electrical stimulation were as good as those for adult animals.

## First multi-channel cochlear implant on a very young child

In 1990, at the time we received approval from the FDA to implant deaf children from two years and above, I was approached by Anne Neame, mother of two-year-old Sian, who was deaf and not receiving the benefit hoped for from a hearing aid (see Chapter 1). She had some residual hearing in one ear, but only in the low frequencies. After careful evaluation with our new Automatic Brainstem Audiometer which gave accurate hearing thresholds, I decided it was a risk we could take. She recovered well from the surgery that Brian and I performed.

It was greatly heartening when Anne observed that Sian took notice of people walking past, and that as time went on her speech improved dramatically. As she grew up, she would talk on the phone and her brothers would complain they could not get a turn.

Sian became a poised young teenager and was introduced to Her Majesty Queen Elizabeth II during the royal visit to the UoM/BEI in 2000. Later, she decided to have an implant in the other ear and said that was the best decision she had ever made. She married, and her language is at such a level that you would not know she had a severe/profound hearing loss. To acknowledge Sian's contributions in helping others to be aware of the benefits of a cochlear implant, the Cochlear Corporation created the Neame Room in the Cochlear Care Centre in Geelong.

I have been truly amazed and delighted by the development of spoken language in young implanted severely/profoundly deaf children who may adapt to electrical stimuli in a different way to those who are post-linguistically deaf. It has been a privilege to follow up many of them and see how their language skills improve over time, enabling them to be fulfilled in their lives.

I am touched by the many parents around the world from different countries, creeds and political systems who have sent messages of gratitude like the one below from Mexico received as this book went to print.

Dear Professor Clark,

My name is Pablo Ruíz and I live in Mexico City. I have a deaf son, his name is Pedro and he is six years old. We implanted Pedro when he was 2 and a half years and now he is able to speak and communicate clearly. He is studying in a bilingual school and he is doing great. He is a happy kid that thanks to you can hear.

I just wanted to thank you and to tell you that your invention has changed our lives.

Pablo

It is thanks also to schools like Mount View and Taralye in Melbourne, the Shepherd Centre in NSW and Hear and Say in Brisbane who have helped those who began as deaf children to integrate with full hearing.

# CHAPTER SIXTEEN

# Creation of the University of Melbourne Bionic Ear Institute

By 1984, I was in need of greater financial support to develop the cochlear implant. This also meant creating a better public profile. I was keener than ever to discover how electrical stimulation of the auditory brain revealed coding mechanisms underlying consciousness. I also felt a responsibility to help Cochlear Ltd become established in the marketplace and be the premier international cochlear implant company. But funds were needed to provide more space, basic equipment, research personnel and support staff for our research at the UoM.

## Creating the University of Melbourne/Bionic Ear Institute

With strong support from Mrs Eve Sher, the Premier, the Honourable Dick Hamer AC, and others, a planning committee was established to decide how to proceed. An inaugural dinner took place on 29 August 1984 to launch an appeal for funds through creating the Australian Bionic Ear Institute (BEI). I had convinced the committee that it should be an institute independent from the RVEEH, so that it was free to develop wider-ranging connections through being affiliated with the UoM. The Dean of Medicine and Vice Chancellor agreed I should lead both entities to develop our research, providing there were no extra costs for the UoM.

Significant donations from trusts and foundations helped get the institute under way. I am most grateful to all the initial board members who gave of their time and expertise to set up the institute's legal and administrative structure. They included Dr James McBride-White, a senior eye surgeon at the RVEEH, who became

**With Queen Beatrix of the Netherlands in the University of Melbourne Department of Otolaryngology on 31 October 1988 on her bicentenary visit to Australia.**

the founding president; Sir Cecil Looker, a former Chair of the Melbourne Stock Exchange, who drafted the constitution; and Mrs Aileen Darke, who led the Women's Auxiliary at the RVEEH.

## Research supported by the University of Melbourne/Bionic Ear Institute

The first annual report of the UoM/BEI in 1986 states that the institute was incorporated on 5 June 1986 with the aim of continuing much-needed further research by the UMDOL. These areas of further research were summarised as discovering the causes and treatment of deafness and the use of neuro-prosthetic devices for those with neurological disorders.[93]

The research areas were:

- recording electrical activity from scalp electrodes to determine how well a child's auditory brain pathways were responding to electrical stimulation of the auditory nerve;

- new testing and training techniques for children receiving bionic ears;

- biological research to determine how to implant a cochlea without losing residual hearing and

- learning how electrical stimulation could achieve speech understanding in background noise.

In addition, research into tactile stimulation of the fingers in children was to be pursued, as results seemed promising.

## Visiting dignitaries

As the research gained momentum and public exposure, we were visited by dignitaries. The Governor of Victoria, Dr Davis McCaughey AC, and his wife Jean showed a special interest in 1987 and visited the UoM/BEI at the UMDOL at the RVEEH. They were followed in 1988 by the Queen of the Netherlands and Prince Claus.

## Purchasing our own building and improving our public profile

It wasn't till some members of the BEI board suggested that we have annual dinners where we could explain the need for money that we made significant progress with our funding and research output. Moreover, the UoM grants and centres had to be accommodated, and so I had to consider purchasing a building for use by both the UoM and the BEI. My prayers were answered when I was put in touch with expert real estate agent Richard Cooksley from Richard Ellis Pty Ltd, and we were able to purchase a suitable building, Mollison House, on the corner of Albert Street and Morrison Place at my limit of $2.2 million. This money came from both the UoM and the BEI. A good friend, Campbell Thorn, did a great job in fitting out the building with a stylish design suitable for showing off our work, as it turned out, to royalty, a president, a governor general, Prime Minister John Howard, governors of Victoria, many politicians, and distinguished clinicians and scientists from overseas.

**Mollison House on Albert Street, Melbourne—the site of the University of Melbourne Bionic Ear Institute in 1990.**

Our patient research was now at street level in Mollison House, and the more sensitive biological research, and where we could have contact with the Jean Littlejohn Deafness Investigation and Research Unit, was kept on the second floor of the RVEEH. Mollison House also meant we had a building where we could host events and, of course, board meetings.

Mrs Jennifer Prescott played a magnificent role in organising the fundraising dinners, while I had to encourage the audience to give generously for the further development of the bionic

**Mr John Gough AO, Mrs Jennifer Prescott, myself, Mrs Janet Calvert-Jones AO and Margaret in 1997.**

ear. This was made easier as there were implanted adults and children who could join me on the podium and share their newfound joy in being able to communicate.

Our profile was improved in 1999 when we became the only research organisation in Australia to receive a visit from the President of China, Mr Jiang Zemin. I was also able to tell him that we had carried out the first multi-channel cochlear implant on a Chinese adult, followed by encouraging outcomes in children.

We were privileged to be visited by Queen Elizabeth II and the Duke of Edinburgh who came for Australia's year 2000 celebrations. The Queen had a special interest in deaf education in the UK. Having safely accompanied them up the fairly precipitous spiral staircase, I introduced our first recipient of the implant, Rod, and first young child recipient, Bryn. Her Majesty was amused to hear that when we played *God Save the Queen* as a hearing test, Rod straight away stood up, pulling all the leads out of his equipment.

Our research was also featured on a postage stamp. The name "Bionic Ear" was given to a lane in East Melbourne running between the UoM in the RVEEH down to Mollison House and is on maps for people doing historic walking tours of the city.

## Further fundraising for the University of Melbourne/Bionic Ear Institute

The UoM/BEI became a focus for donations and gratefully acknowledged the many organisations and individuals who funded us. The Victorian Lions Foundation continued their generous support for the two Lions Research Fellows, Pam Dawson and Peter Busby, who continued their research to see how young children could best develop spoken language. We had an anonymous donor establish the Hearing Research Foundation, which enabled Julia Wunderlich to examine how brain electrical activity reflects the ability to process speech. The Mazda Foundation supported Vanessa Surowiecki's research, showing the importance of attention, memory and thinking in developing language. We were delighted to receive support from Ziggy Switkowski, CEO of Telstra, who even ran a

**Sian Neame being introduced to Queen Elizabeth II when she came to visit the Bionic Ear Institute in 2000.**

telethon for us. In April 2002, Sir Roderick Carnegie AC, a distinguished industrialist and his wife Carmen, who had a deaf grandson, hosted a marvellous occasion in the beautiful gardens of their home at Woodend out of Melbourne. Carmen worked very hard to engage her friends in an event that was best described as a country fair. As an added draw card, they had a golf competition run by Peter Thompson, Australia's famous golfer. The funds raised enabled me to appoint scientist Rachael Richardson to explore the possibility of getting the nerves in the inner ear to grow again. This could create a radically improved bionic ear by providing more nerves to stimulate. The Stavros Niarchos Foundation enabled me to appoint Dr Andrew Wise to study the neural connections and show a clear picture of the complicated nerve in the inner ear being stimulated with an advanced cochlear implant.

## Money to retire

When approaching the age of 70 years, I was due to relinquish my Chair of Otolaryngology at the UoM in 2004, as I had agreed previously with the then Dean of Medicine, Professor Richard Larkins.

There was only $2.5 million in reserve to sustain the position of a Professor/Director of the UoM/BEI after using as much as possible for ongoing research. So, when I received the Prime Minister's Prize for Science of $300,000 later in 2004, I offered to donate it to the institute if enough donors could be found to match it to a total of $6 million. When no one came forward, Prime Minister John Howard AC found a way of contributing the $6 million required.

I had been asked at planning retreats to plot the future direction for the UoM/BEI. After discussions with the new Dean of Medicine, Professor Jim Angus, we agreed that the BEI would be best as an independent body having a director chosen with university representation on the selection committee. The successful applicant would also be appointed as an adjunct professor at the UoM in a new discipline, Medical Bionics. Jim Angus and Gerry Moriarty proposed the BEI be renamed the Graeme Clark Institute, and the Prime Minister was pleased to announce this when he made a formal visit to the institute in April 2005.

It was agreed that I stay on as the director of the BEI for the year 2005 and help with its management till a successor was appointed. After my retirement from the UoM/BEI that decision was not carried out, and I was asked to approve the renaming of the UoM/BEI as simply the Bionics Institute.

Fortunately, I had already commenced leading the bionics section of the Intelligent Polymer Research Institute of Professor Gordon Wallace's ARC Centre of Excellence for Electromaterials Science based at the University of Wollongong (UoW). So after leaving the BEI at the end of 2005, I was able to set up a research laboratory in the Daley wing of St Vincent's Hospital with Dr Mark Cook (now Professor) and made some progress in how to restore spinal cord function for people who were paralysed. I left at the end of 2008 when a further opportunity arose to learn more about electrophysiology of cochlear implantation with Tony Paolini, whom I had trained, and was set up at La Trobe University (LTU). When that university offered me a three-year tenured post, I was deeply grateful and thereafter had some fruitful collaborations with Tony and others. We were able to show in the experimental animal the value of inserting an electrode close to the ganglion cells by hugging the central column.

In 2007, when Rod sadly died, leaving his temporal bones for research, I knew I must engage with a number of staff at LTU to examine them. We showed that the first cochlear array had been difficult to extract because fractures in his temporal bone had caused a proliferation of bone around it. But the new electrode inserted by Associate Professor Robert Briggs had gone in well and there were no subsequent difficulties.

In 2011, my three-year term at LTU ended, all too soon. I also ran the risk of losing my personal assistant, Debbie Mussett.

Then, I believed my prayers were answered when another door opened. In 2012, I was invited to return to the UoM, this time in the Engineering Department, to a new centre, National Informa-

**The bionic ear stamp commemorating an Australian development in bioengineering 1988.**

tion and Communications Technology, Australia. This proved to be the right time for the next phase of research. I was able to work closely with Professor John Furness FAA (Professor in Anatomy) to study the effect of the electrodes on Rod's cochlea, and with histopathologist and son Dr Jonathan Clark to study the nature and effects of dark deposits in the tissue. These were shown by the electron beam from the synchrotron at Clayton to be platinum, but with no adverse effects on Rod. While with National Information and Communications Technology, I had the opportunity to collaborate with friend and speech scientist Terry Caelli and the group at LTU on new directions in speech analyses for the cochlear implant. As before, when the funding dried up at the end of 2013, the Dean of Engineering, Professor Iven Mareels, made provision for financial remuneration for Debbie to continue while I said I would be prepared to be *pro bono*. Working with engineering colleagues has produced new ideas that would possibly be useful for Cochlear Ltd. It has also been exciting that the university has created an institute for biomedical engineering to extend the work with cochlear implants to other areas of neurology and neuroscience, as discussed in the next chapter.

CHAPTER SEVENTEEN

# New horizons

The multi-channel cochlear implant has meant that severely/profoundly deaf people can understand significant amounts of running speech without the need to lipread. The implants have become smaller and more reliable, and the failure rate is low. Wireless technology enables implantees to listen to television and communicate with others, including those in their clinic, using a smartphone. The implant package has been designed for MRI to be used without having to remove the magnet. The speech processors are waterproofed for swimming, but the most practical solution for helping people engage in regular activities unhindered will be to eliminate the external component completely and to have a totally implantable cochlear implant.

There are still challenges to ensure all severely/profoundly deaf people receive high fidelity hearing, appreciate music and understand speech well in background noise. Our original patient Rod Saunders expressed this well when I interviewed him in 2007. Rod said, "As far as speech is concerned, it is very close; but with music, it is way off."

## The Graeme Clark Foundation

The audiology section of the UMDOL grew in the late 1980s, in part due to the advent of cochlear implants for adults and children, but we had to recoup the costs of managing this through health services. The funds went first into a special personal account. Then, in 1991, we formed a company called Audio Med to manage this work in a more business-like manner and pay for staff in the Cochlear Implant Clinic at the RVEEH. We used any surplus to support ongoing research. On 17 October 2005, I chaired a meeting of Audio Med to change the organisation to become a company limited by guarantee after an increase in government

**In 2015 I received the Russ Prize, which recognises a bioengineering achievement in widespread use that improves the human condition.**

support meant that we would not be needing to pay for staff engaged in our audiological and implant activities.

With interest from friends Kimberley Smith, David Burt and others in 2007, we changed the organisation to a not-for-profit charitable organisation named Nerve and Deafness Inc. (later Nerve Deafness Inc.). I raised some money speaking at church breakfasts, through receiving significant donations from some who knew of my work and the sale of a DVD on my Christian and scientific journey at Christian bookshops.

But we needed more substantial support to be making a difference, and in 2007 the board was addressed by fundraising consultant Roger Thornton, who advised changing the name of the organisation to the Graeme Clark Foundation. The decision was ratified in 2008 when Jerry Ellis AO, former Chancellor of MU and CEO of BHP, took over as Chair. Friend David Jack, well-known for his art on buildings in the city, designed our logo.

By May 2008, our reserves had increased to approximately $600,000, which helped us to be a "doing" rather than a "receiving" body. We used a donation from the Inner Wheel Club in Baulkham Hills, Sydney to purchase essential equipment for the spinal cord research in the bionics research at the St Vincent's Hospital. A sum of $6,000 went to John Huigen to scope the Aboriginal communities to see how we might be able to prevent the terrible incidence of middle ear infection, $10,000 was given to help a young severely/profoundly deaf boy in Peru called Luis get a cochlear implant and $30,000 over three years was given to Dr Mary John to do further studies on Aboriginal ear infections, overseen by Professor Stephen O'Leary. Mary has continued to also work on creating a cochlear implant centre at the Christian Medical College in Vellore in India.

Then UoM wanted funds to establish a Chair of Audiology and Speech Science in perpetuity. Could I help? The question was put to the board and as there was such good research being done by Professor Richard Dowell and staff, we agreed to make a gift of $600,000. Although that radically reduced our coffers, we all felt it was very worthwhile to continue the Foundation, and I was able to help with a bequest to pay for overheads.

It is pleasing that funds from the GCF have helped Professor Dowell and team in four years to publish over 50 scientific articles in leading journals. The research findings include reports on the importance of cochlear implantation in young children, the perception and production of tone in children who speak Mandarin and Cantonese, and the preservation of hearing in people who have a cochlear implant. It has also helped cement the relationship between the UoM and the RVEEH, with Richard's appointment as the clinic director.

In June 2018, I stood down as Chair in favour of Grant Holley, an experienced lawyer whom all members were very confident would be an excellent replacement. At the same meeting, David Burt LIB, who had been a staunch supporter, and the secretary/treasurer since the beginning, resigned for health reasons. To assist in achieving its new vision, I requested that the GCF use the $50,000 bequest from a friend Joan Kaye for administrative purposes to maintain the foundation. It was pleasing that donations were coming in to create a fund named Sounds of Simone to allow poor children in India to receive a cochlear implant. Furthermore, under the leadership of Professor Stephen O'Leary and the late Captain Peter Kentley, the Foundation has fostered a strong interest in science in Victorian schools.

## The Graeme Clark Institute for Biomedical Engineering

The cochlear implant has also helped pave the way for many advances in biomedical engineering, supported through the Graeme Clark Institute (GCI) for Biomedical Engineering established at the UoM in 2016. The GCI led by Professor Mark Cook currently helps coordinate research programs. The disciplines are bioelectronics and neuro-engineering, biomaterials, regenerative medicine and personalised implants, and computational modelling for cardiovascular diseases.

## Advanced cochlear implants

Advanced cochlear implants need to transmit even more information through the electro-neural interface or "bottleneck" between the world of sound and the central nervous system through new speech codes and electrode bundles. Artificial intelligence may play an important role in differentiating the speech signal from background noise. A totally implantable cochlear implant is being developed by Cochlear Ltd to allow people to be less self-conscious about the implant and participate more easily in a variety of sports. The totally implantable cochlear implant will have the microphone or sound transducer, speech processor and

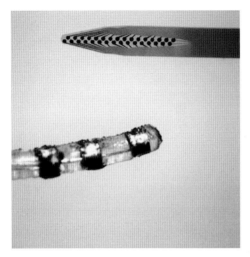

**An early banded electrode array (bottom) compared with a thin-film sputtered electrode (top) developed in collaboration with Professor Antonio Paolini, La Trobe University.**

receiver-stimulator with electrode array as well as a rechargeable battery all implanted beneath the skin. The person will wear nothing to indicate they have had difficulty hearing.

To improve the temporal and spatial coding of sound, it is necessary to more accurately reproduce the pattern of neural activity occurring in groups of nerve fibres. This requires reproducing the fine patterns of nerve stimulation using smaller electrodes that maintain safe charge densities by enlarged active surface areas through electrochemical and other "roughening" procedures. An alternative is to use carbon, which is biologically nonreactive, to conduct electrical current. Graphene tracks can be deposited on Silastic, PTFE (Teflon) or other biocompatible material and connected to platinum sputtered on the other side of an electrode carrier.

Carbon nanotubes can be used to keep the charge density at safe levels and provide increased points of electrical stimulation. They are so small that 1,000 of them can be stacked next to a human hair, and they conduct electricity like metal. We have also found them to be biocompatible.

There is a possibility of sensing sound vibrations with a totally implantable cochlear implant. A small microphone is implanted under the skin behind the ear or in the external auditory canal, an accelerometer is attached to the ossicles, a piezo-electric cantilever converts bending movement into electrical signals and a device on the medial wall of the middle ear is designed to transmit and receive infrared light from a reflector on the eardrum. These are now all possible with advances in microelectronics and micro-machines which can make devices smaller than a house dust mite or grass pollen.

Cochlear Ltd has already developed a prototype totally implantable cochlear implant which is being trialled in a small group of volunteers with encouraging results.

## Restoration of function after spinal cord injury

In 2000, I extended our work on cochlear implants to other areas of biomedical engineering. I first collaborated with Gordon Wallace from the UoW on the use of intelligent polymers, not only for advanced cochlear implant electrode arrays, but for the restoration of function after spinal cord injuries.

At first it was necessary to know if the neurons below the damaged section remained viable so that they could be connected to pathways above. The pathways transmit motor function downward and sensory function from below upwards.

Fortunately, Byron Kakulus from Perth had a large collection of spinal cords in his department. A small number had gross cystic lesions, but a majority had neurons that appeared to be viable.

**A forest of carbon nanotubes with a coating of polypyrole. Each nanotube is one-thousandth the width of a human hair. Prepared by the Australian Research Council's Centre of Excellence for Electromaterial Science at the University of Wollongong.**

That encouraged my ARC team to proceed with this research direction.

Research was then needed to learn what factors are released at the site of injury that either promote or impair recovery. The substances that facilitate spinal cord repair can be identified and instilled, while those that slow it down can be regulated. In the bionics program of an ARC Centre of Excellence, my team studied how the good proteins can be incorporated into intelligent plastic scaffolds and then released with the passage of an electrical current. This will facilitate nerve growth across the damaged segment of the spinal cord.

**The Stentrode is inserted into a blood vessel in the brain and passed to be near the motor cortex to record electrical activity in the brain.**

Next, we needed to see if adult stem cells could be converted to neurons and grow on a scaffold across the gap.

An alternative approach is to record electrical activity from the brain, determine its meaning and use the information to activate limbs or prostheses. An electrode to do this has been developed by an Australian neurologist Thomas Oxley. This electrode is called the Stentrode. This can be inserted into a blood vessel in the brain and passed to be near the motor cortex. The motor cortex has different parts of the body represented spatially like a person (homunculus). It is hoped that when the paralysed person wishes to walk, the thought generates electrical activity in the region of the leg and can activate the muscles for walking by an electronic device connected to the nerves for the muscles. Alternatively, Dr John Donoghue and team from Brown University inserted 100 hair-thin electrodes—like a micro-toothbrush—into the brain of a group of people with quadriplegia. A computer analysed the neural responses to their thoughts, and they could move a cursor around a TV screen at will, were able to operate a robotic arm and hand and could drive a wheelchair.

## Loss of vision and the bionic eye

In the 1960s, electrical stimulation of the visual pathways to relieve blindness was undertaken about the same time as electrical stimulation of the auditory system to relieve deafness. These two sensory systems are, however, different in structure and function. The auditory system has four main processing stations before the cerebral cortex, and the visual system one. The auditory system processes temporal information to a greater degree than the visual system.

On the other hand, spatial recognition is of prime importance in the visual system where there are over one million nerve fibres in the optic nerve and an equivalent number in the primary visual cortex. This could explain why an industrial cochlear implant was achieved in 1985 and a clinically effective visual device has not yet emerged due to the difficulty of interfacing a high number of electrodes to the visual pathways. Central vision is processed by the macula at the back of the eyeball, a circular area with a diameter of about 3 mm that transmits about half a million points of light for central vision. It has complex innerva-

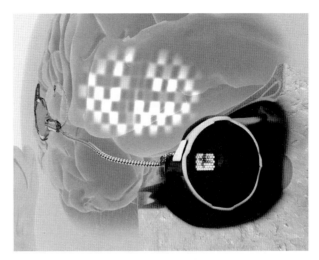

**An implanted device stimulating an area at the back of the eyeball with the pattern appearing in the visual cortex.**

tion for colour vision and rapidly moving objects, like a cricket ball moving at over 60 km/h. The development of the cochlear implant could be said to have paved the way for engineering a bionic eye.

The challenge is to provide enough points of light for visual acuity in the first instance. There are two approaches to coding the visual scene. The first approach is stimulating the optic nerve in the eyeball and the second approach is stimulating the visual cortex.

The device receives signals from a camera fitted to a pair of glasses. The camera sends the visual information to a separate processor. The processor breaks the image down into pixels and sends key features to a silicon chip, by wireless. Professor Anthony Burkitt from the Department of Engineering, UoM has been leading the development of a processor to simulate what the image could be like.

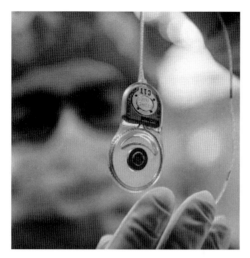

**Based on the bionic ear, the Minder is implanted under the scalp in order to monitor brain activity and anticipate epileptic seizures. This is being studied by the Department of Neurology at St Vincent's Hospital under Professor Mark Cook and the Bionics Institute.**

A large number of people with blindness have optic atrophy which means there is significant loss of the nerve fibres to the brain. For that reason there is a greater need for a bionic eye to be implanted on the visual cortex.

## The treatment of drug-resistant epilepsy

Epilepsy is characterised by seizures that can be of short or long duration. They may occur over a limited time or be lifelong. Approximately 3% of Australians will experience epilepsy and over 250,000 Australians currently have the condition. Approximately 40% of those with epilepsy are children. More than two thirds become seizure-free with medication, but it is a very disabling condition.

Research being led by Professor Cook, Director of the GCI, is aiming to monitor the electrical activity of the brain through scalp electrodes and thus detect the onset of a seizure. The Bionics Institute, St Vincent's Hospital Melbourne and the UoM, in conjunction with a founding investment from Cochlear Ltd, have developed a minimally invasive device, Minder, to record EEGs over a period of months or years. Minder will assist neurologists in the diagnosis and treatment of epilepsy. It is hoped this innovation will not only lead to accurate diagnosis of the onset of a seizure, but its reversal.

## Biomaterials, bio-fabrication and regenerative medicine

These studies help determine how implanted materials connect to the body tissue, are free of infection and deliver therapeutic chemicals or stem cells. Personalised implants are achieved by 3D printing of implantable body parts and devices.

All body implants can result in infection. In the USA, the Centres for Disease Control estimates that two million people have hospital-acquired infections each year and 99,000 die. About 35% are due to catheters and pacemakers which aid the infection. The infection may be prevented or controlled if the implants are coated with intelligent plastics incorporating antibiotics or other anti-bacterial agents to be released at the appropriate time.

Bio-fabrication, using 3D printing, creates personalised implants that can make precise replacements of bone after cranial and bone surgery. It will also facilitate the management of advanced osteoarthritis, tumour resection, trauma and congenital abnormalities.

## Computational modelling for cardiovascular diseases

Computer modelling of the cardiovascular system with simulation of pulsatile blood flow will assist with the reconstruction of arteries, the design and placement of stents and the management of arrhythmias. This will have a major impact on the treatment of heart disease.

One important application is the evaluation of the heart musculature and electrophysiology after a coronary occlusion. This can lead to scarring and abnormal cardiac rhythms. Modern treatment now can introduce electrodes into the heart and coagulate the regions responsible for dangerous rhythm changes. This is now possible with much greater accuracy using three-dimensional functional MRI. It is also helping manage congenital defects.

# CHAPTER EIGHTEEN

# Reflections on the journey: Leadership and spiritual growth

## Directing research

Before I took up my position as Professor of Otolaryngology, I attended a course in business management. This proved helpful in leading the research programs, but there was nothing written specifically on that subject, so I had to learn on the job. The ability to interrelate disciplines was a skill I had acquired at medical school, but I needed to create a team effort. As a leader I needed to encourage cooperation amongst all members and motivate everyone to strive for the vision that I had.

In research, good ideas are at a premium. There are many good projects that add knowledge or confirm hitherto established findings. The big breakthroughs that change thinking or produce products that dominate markets are rarer.

In a group, people are reluctant to share ideas in case they get "stolen." For that reason, I found it desirable to lead by example and share my ideas. To develop insights, I spent time reading the literature and letting the imagination run loose. But it is not enough to have good ideas if they are not tested and remain as suggestions. I like to think of discoveries as involving five "I"s: imagination, which leads to inspiration, then innovation, followed by investment and finally industrial development. Imagination is forming concepts of external objects; as Albert Einstein said: "Imagination is more important than knowledge. Knowledge is limited. Imagination encircles the world." Inspiration is developing the imagined concepts into good ideas. Innovation is finding ways to apply those good ideas. Investment is required to

**Bushwalking with Jonathan, Roslyn and Merran on the Cathedral Range in Victoria in 1985.**

take innovation through to proof of concept. Lastly, industry is needed to develop the ideas for widespread use.

So, from a pragmatic point of view, I was keen to share my ideas to advance the research project. A suggestion could come at home, during a discussion in the lab or a walk down the corridor. As other directors have agreed, ideas may come back six months later more effectively minted and owned. In this case one simply has to say, "That's a good idea", and not argue who thought of the key idea first. I learned the best approach was to engender trust and create a melting pot of ideas that all could feel they had a hand in creating.

It was clear to me that the director should set the tone for the group. I was passionate about making discoveries that would provide exciting new knowledge, not only focussed on developing speech understanding for deaf children and adults, but knowledge about how the brain functioned. It was said at the time there were two remaining frontiers in medicine: the restoration of brain function and genetic engineering.

Being young and energetic, I wanted to be challenged and I also had faith in the young people who were being attracted to the project. We worked hard and we played hard. That is evident in the enthusiasm given to creative performances at our Christmas concerts. Many who were there said it was the best time of their lives.

At the time, there was a clear distinction between pure and applied research. Pure research was curiosity-driven and seen as the ultimate goal, and any research that had an implied intent was considered impure. Louis Pasteur would disagree. He maintained research was not pure or applied, only good or bad. I came to that view in balancing my research between coding speech with electrical stimulation of the brain on the one hand and trying to understand the bases of human consciousness on the other.

I have learned it is essential to strive for excellence even though perfection cannot be achieved. It has been said that a few years' effort should see a positive outcome. If I had said to those joining the team, "You may need to dedicate at least a decade, or possibly a lifetime," some might have had second thoughts. They would need to say, "Never say never," believing that an outcome would be achieved.

From the beginning, I decided I would not pursue the research with the aim of making money, which can impair judgement. I received my entitlements to royalties but did not purchase shares when they came on the market, partly because I was too busy doing the work and I missed out on the first offers! I was grateful, however, when the owner of Nucleus, Paul Trainor, gave me and some others shares in Pacific Dunlop. I have not experienced before, or since, that level of generosity by an industrialist.

Honesty is a trait I realised was vital in our research. The international community needs to know that the data has been accurately recorded without bias. Patient, hospital and industry depended on it. Being prepared to prove oneself wrong makes one more objective. The bigger the leap forward, the greater the need for proof, which must be accompanied by independent expert review. Finally, as Louis Pasteur said, "Pure science in its highest form cannot make any progress without industrial application benefitting sooner or later from its precious results."

It has been a privilege to become a friend to some of my patients, none more so than Rod Saunders. We shared a few speaking engagements, and at a conference in San Antonio, he was delighted that he had a queue almost as long as mine waiting for him to sign my book *Sounds from Silence*. His confidence was on display when he gave an introductory address for a presentation of mine to the Governor of Victoria, Professor David de Kretser AC, at Government House. Rod said:

> Don't let Professor Clark fool you. When Graeme first proposed the bionic ear, he acted as if he was doing me a big favour by restoring my ability to hear. Little did I know then that this seemingly humble person had his own sneaky agenda. From the moment my implant was perfected, this man has been sending me on public speaking engagements. I've spoken to the Queen of the Netherlands, the Queen of England, that bloke who used to be the Prime Minister and earlier this year, he had me fronting an audience of 800 in San Antonio, Texas. I've also had to face some gruelling interviews ranging from Mel and Kochie to a former Miss America—who, incidentally, let me wear her tiara. However, the most probing questions as to the quality of Graeme's workmanship came from the Duke of Edinburgh when he asked me whether I sparked in the shower.

I was not certain, but I felt pretty sure that Graeme and his team would have used quality insulating tape. The implant has, however, put a spark in the lives of many deaf people.

## Reviewing my journey with Jesus Christ

At the end of 1966, the fact that I had arthritis in the cervical spine played a part in my deciding to leave ENT practice and go back to the UoS to do a PhD in neurophysiology. I had prayed for healing, but that did not happen. Instead, I read a research paper by American surgeon Blair Simmons, who had stimulated a deaf person's auditory nerve electrically. Even though this patient heard sound but not speech, it lit a fire in my belly. I dared to hope I could cure nerve deafness in adults and children. Looking back now, I believe there was an unseen guiding hand correcting my mistakes and career choices. In a way it has been like Bunyan's *The Pilgrim's Progress*. Christian had a dream to find the Celestial City. He first had to go through the Wicket Gate and was falsely advised by Mr Worldly Wiseman. He was corrected by Evangelist and held to the promise Jesus made in Matthew 7:8: "For everyone who asks receives, and he who seeks finds, and to him who knocks, the door will be open." On Christian's journey there were many trials—Hill Difficulty, Giant Despair's dungeon, the temptations of Vanity Fair. But there were characters like Hopeful and Faithful who helped him finally reach his goal.

In 1970, when I commenced at the UoM as the youngest clinical professor, like my colleague Gerard Crock, Professor of Ophthalmology, I became part of the so-called town/gown division. We supposedly had an unpractical academic outlook, whereas our colleagues considered themselves more practised in the surgical arts. Although I was qualified in general surgery as well as ENT, I was consistently criticised.[94] My only recourse was to try our Lord's command in Matthew 5:4: "But I tell you again: love your enemies and pray for those who persecute you." This gave me great peace and allowed me to continue my research without worrying about what people thought of me or seeking personal glory, though that did not seem likely at the time; the reviewers for my NHMRC grants considered that electrical stimulation of the auditory nerve would not work, and some were even opposed to it. Such was the general climate of opinion.

I was encouraged in my Christian faith by many people, not least by the late Professor Donald MacCrimmon Mackay from the University of Keele in the UK. He came out in 1972 as the Australian Vice Chancellor's Speaker. He had a brilliant intellect, had been Reader in Theoretical Physics at London University and then Professor of Communication and Neuroscience at the University of Keele with a strong interest in brain function of the visual system. He also wrote scholarly articles on logic and theology. I attended all his addresses, which convinced me that science was not necessarily in conflict with the Bible.

When I failed to get NHMRC grant money, Donald advised me not to spread studies too thinly but concentrate on my main line of investigation: the electrical stimulation of the auditory brain to replicate the sound of speech. For this, I would have to buy expensive equipment. Not having thousands of dollars, I prayed for help. But I had learned that God did not always answer prayers the way I wanted, and I commenced a more systematic study of the Scriptures with the help of commentaries. I found passages of Scripture like Luke 18:7: "Will not God bring about justice for his chosen ones who cry out to him day and night?" For many months I prayed daily for God's will to be done. Then, out of the blue, Sir Reginald Ansett, the owner of a television station, contacted me and offered to run a telethon to raise funds for the research. This led to two major telethons and two minor ones between 1973 and 1976. Without that money, it would have been impossible to develop the UoM prototype receiver-stimulator to discover how to code speech with electrical stimulation.

At this time, I also realised I could not be a hidden Christian. I also knew that I would be judged more strictly, and that I would have to be scrupulously fair and unbiased. Not wanting to be an evangelist or proselytise, I simply placed a Jesus sticker on the back window of our battered Toyota Corolla hatchback. Then I found I was not alone. One of the staff, Ray Black, offered to organise prayer and Bible study in my office and other Christians joined in, sometimes as many as 13 out of 50 staff. The group spontaneously prayed for peace and guidance on a range of issues, including the cochlear implant, and I found that faith and fellowship with others helped sustain me in a stressful and demanding workplace.

In 1972, we were attending the Methodist church in Eltham. One Sunday, it was announced that Rumanian pastor Richard Wurmbrand was speaking that afternoon in Camberwell about the persecution of Christians in communist lands. Margaret and I felt we had to go, and somehow got there with our four children, with one-year-old Merran sleeping right through the address. Wurmbrand himself had been imprisoned for 14 years for refusing to agree Stalin was "the light of the world." Afterwards, we read some of his books, including *Tortured for Christ*, which were challenging indeed.

As a result, I made contact with Anglican Canon Michael Bordeaux, who spoke Russian and had set up Keston College in the London School of Economics for the study of persecution in Russia. Later, I was able to raise funds for Michael to come to Australia and speak to the Australian Council of Churches leaders and at the UoM so that people could have a greater understanding of the conflicts. The persecution of Christians across the world has only worsened, and more recently we have felt drawn to support the Barnabas Fund modelled on Keston College and set up by Canon Patrick and Rosemary Sookhdeo with headquarters in England. The courage of Christians suffering injustices inspires and puts us to shame. How much harder it is for them to keep their faith.

Looking back over our time in Eltham, we began in 1972 with six years in the Methodist Church, a couple in the Anglican, and then turned to the Presbyterians for a deeper study of the Bible. After nearly 20 years with our friends there who supported us with their prayers during the hardest times of the implant development, we went to Doncaster City Church to experience more of the Holy Spirit. Here we have stayed, even though we do not agree with their interpretation of some parts of the Bible, including Genesis 1 and 2. That disagreement need not stop us making every effort to live in peace with all men, as Hebrews 12:14 tells us.

After the implant was a success, I was asked by a reporter what had kept me going through such a difficult time. I explained that it was my wife, team, friends, doggedness and faith in God. He seemed surprised that a scientist doing productive research could be a believer in a supernatural God. It was felt in some circles that admitting to a belief in God was committing intellectual suicide, but I was on a journey to find out the truth and I certainly needed God's help. I had been criticised heavily for what I was doing, so what did a little more criticism matter?

## Other scientists who relate science and Christian faith

Even so, many scientists were atheistic, so I still asked myself if it was irrational to believe. I read the book *Religion and the Rise of Modern Science* by Reijer Hooykaas. This explained how the first scientists (like Boyle, Hook, Faraday, Newton and Pascal) based their theories on observation and experimentation but saw no reason to abandon their belief in God. "This most beautiful system of the sun, planets and comets could only proceed from the counsel and dominion of an intelligent and powerful being," wrote Isaac Newton. And Galileo did not abandon his belief in God either when he discovered the sun did not move across the sky "like a champion rejoicing to run his course." He did not see this poetical expression in Psalm 19 as in conflict with science.

The astonishing finding of the Big Bang is in accord with Genesis 1: "In the beginning, God created the heavens and the earth." Whereas scientists including Albert Einstein once believed the universe had no beginning, they came to accept the findings that it arose in an instant. Furthermore, in Genesis 1:2 we read that the Spirit of God was hovering over the waters, and scientists seem to be in agreement about the presence of water early on in some form without knowing why.

One of the many scientists who believe in God is Sir John Polkinghorne, former Professor of Theoretical Physics at Cambridge and co-discoverer of quarks, the building blocks of matter. As Sir John Polkinghorne has said, the evidence that conditions were made just right for life is enough for him to believe God made all for a purpose.[95]

Each new finding in science increases my awe at the perfection of the creation. Physicist and atheist Fred Hoyle was surprised with his findings of the way elements were created. He stated, "The laws of nuclear physics have been deliberately designed with regard to the consequences that they produce inside stars … part of a deep-laid scheme."

Just how life emerged is not clear, but it required the genetic code—DNA or RNA—which are words, or to a believer, God's instructions. This is the view of Francis Collins,[96] who headed the Human Genome Project. This genetic code is needed for creating proteins, the basis of life. Formerly atheist British philosopher Anthony Frew came to believe in a God when he marvelled at the complexity behind the simple statement in Genesis 1:11, "God said: 'Let the land produce seed-bearing plants.'"

## Evolution and a Christian faith

When it comes to evolution, atheist scientists like Jacques Monod have used the phrase "chance and necessity" to explain the mechanism. However, Professor Donald Mackay's answer to Monod is:

> To personify "chance" as if we were talking about a causal agent "free but blind", is to switch from a scientific to a quasi-religious mythological concept. To proceed to claim scientific authority for describing this as a central concept of biology is to compound confusion. To dress up the result as if it were "observed and tested fact," that was at odds with all concepts of divine immanence in natural events is little short of dishonest.[97]

If the events underlyingevolution are random, then one would not expect it to be possible to rerun evolution and converge on the same outcome. Conway Morris, Professor of Paleobiology (the biology of fossil animals and plants) at Cambridge University, gives many examples of convergence (that is, repeated evolution in independent lineages of the same biochemical pathway or organ or structure).[98] For example, compound and camera eyes have evolved more than twenty different times, from the octopus to the human. Retaining the egg in the mother, prior to a live birth, has evolved one hundred times separately among lizards and snakes alone, and marsupials have evolved separately in Australia and South America. Denis Alexander says in his book:

> So, we are living in an ordered universe, not at all a random universe, but an anthropically fruitful one in which there is a biological narrative culminating in us as its observers.[99]

## The brain, consciousness and Christian faith

Surely the climax of evolution is the human brain with its 100,000 million nerve cells, each connected to up to 10,000 other brain cells, enabling us to reason, calculate, process information, store memories, control movement, find meaning, think independent thoughts, make decisions and feel emotions. Frances Crick, co-discoverer of the structure of DNA, says in his book *The Astonishing Hypothesis* that the great challenge of the 21st century is "understanding what it is that develops in the brain of the human embryo that gives rise to consciousness."

It has been argued that our conscious experiences are nothing more than electrical events in the brain, as though our brain were a supercomputer. In this scenario, we would have no free will; every response would be determined for us by the pattern of electrical activity. This view has a number of flaws referred to in my ABC Boyer lectures in 2007. The brain functions differently from a computer; we can reflect internally. Our feelings such as love, hate and so on cannot be explained simply as the workings of electrical currents and the chemistry of the brain. If all our thoughts are predetermined, then we could never be sure that any of our conclusions were independent. Distinguished neuroscientist Sir John Eccles said in his 1965 Boyer lecture:

> I wish to do all I can to restore to mankind the sense of wonder and mystery that arises
> from the attempt to face up to the reality of our very existence as conscious beings.

In my journey to discover meaning in life and a personal relationship with Jesus Christ, I felt it necessary to be as sure as possible that science and belief were compatible. I had also to test these beliefs in the vagaries of life and not rely on a set of rules to be obeyed.

It was becoming clear to me from scientists' analyses of the physical and biological universe there was increasing evidence for intelligence behind this creation. But who or what is this intelligence? Some said it was nothing but chance and selection of the best solution. Like many, I felt confident there was a supernatural being we call God. But was God a distant force, or one that could be related to in a personal way? The answer to this is in the Bible, which I realised is an account of the relationship between God and the Jews extended through Christ to the world.

It is not primarily a rule book but a guide for all to know God. And, it needs to be made clear. The language can be factual, figurative, or symbolic, but it is above all about the relationship of a supernatural God with his people. Understanding the importance of the language of the Bible is not always appreciated. An excellent account is given by Dr J. A. Thompson in his book *Genesis 1–3: Science? History? Theology?* published by ISCAST/Acorn. I cannot do better than quote this recommendation by Allan J. Day, Emeritus Professor of Physiology from the UoM.

> In an area often charged with misconceptions and problems, John Thompson cuts through to the heart of the science–theology issues presented by the Genesis narrative. His clear exposition answers many of the questions thoughtful Christians feel guilty to raise that often go unanswered, while the literary approach to the text is both scholarly and evangelical. The assertion that Genesis is neither history nor science but sets forth in unmistakable terms certain great affirmations about God, humankind and the world cannot be over-emphasised.

Finally, the question that bothers many is whether this personal God is one who loves the creation. Can this be so when we see so much cruelty and suffering around us? For me, the most pertinent answer is that God, through the suffering, death and resurrection of Jesus on the cross, has shown that love.

In reflecting on my journey, I can only say I have had moments when I have wanted to be my own master and pursue my own goals. I have empathy for those who have a materialistic, atheistic view of life. But, with reverence, I believe God, through Jesus Christ, has guided me all my life and enabled me to bring a new life to severely/profoundly deaf people.

# Graeme Clark Orators

The Graeme Clark Orations are an initiative of Luan Ismahil through the creation of the Convergence Science Network which is providing an open forum for leading scientists to share their interdisciplinary research that will lead to major breakthroughs.

**2008.** Laureate Professor Graeme Clark AC, *A Partnership in Research Leading to the Bionic Ear and Beyond*, University of Melbourne and Graeme Clark Institute for Biomedical Research.

**2010.** Dr Craig Venter, *Writing the Genetic Code*, founder of the J. Craig Venter Institute, co-discoverer of the human genome, first synthetic cells and immune targets to responses to novel coronavirus.

**2011.** Francis Crick Professor Terrence Sejnowski, *The Computational Brain*, Director of the Crick-Jacobs Centre for Computational Neurobiology, Salk Institute.

**2012.** Dame Linda Partridge, *Forever Young*, Professor of Biometry, Evolution and Environment, University College London.

**2013.** Mr Geoff Lamb, *Global Health, Economic Growth and the End of Absolute Poverty: Hopeful Evidence and Hard Challenges*, Managing Director of Public Policy, Bill & Melinda Gates Foundation.

**2014.** Professor Don Ingber, *The Next Technology Wave: Biologically Inspired Engineering*, Founding Director of Biologically Inspired Engineering, Harvard University.

**2015.** Sir Paul Nurse, *Controlling How Cells Reproduce*, Director of the Francis Crick Institute and won the Nobel Prize in 2001 through showing the special gene involved in cell division.

**2016.** Dr Tom Insel, *Science and Technology: New Frontiers for Helping People with Mental Illness*, led the National Institute for Mental Health, and has shown how special care can improve the outcome for first psychotic episodes.

**2017.** Professor Harold Varmus, *Transitions in Cancer Research*, Weill Cornell Medicine New York, former Director National Institutes of Health and National Cancer Centre. He won the Nobel Prize in 1989 for discovering the retroviral origin of oncogenes.

**2018.** Professor Paula Hammond, *Nano Medicine Comes of Age: How Engineered Materials are Transforming Medical Treatment*, Head of Laboratory at the Massachusetts Institute of Technology (MIT) Koch Institute for Integrative Cancer Research, leading research with nanoparticles (1/1000 diameter human hair) that target and kill cancer cells.

**2019.** Professor Tim Denison, *Towards an Electronic Prescription*, Professor of Biomedical Electrical Medicine at the University of Oxford. Leading research on how to record and reverse electrical malfunction from the brain e.g. with deep brain stimulation for epilepsy, chronic pain and Parkinson's Disease.

# Bibliography

Ainsworth, W. A. *Mechanisms of Speech Recognition.* Oxford: Pergamon Press, 1976.

Allitt, B. J., Harris, A. R., Morgan, S. J., Clark, G. M. and Paolini, A. G. "Thin-Film Micro-Electrode Stimulation of the Cochlea in Rats Exposed to Aminoglycoside Induced Hearing Loss." *Hearing Research* 331 (2016): 13–26.

Black, R. C., and G. M. Clark. "Electrical Transmission Line Properties of the Cat Cochlea." *Proceedings of the Australian Physiological and Pharmacological Society* 8 (1977).

Black, R. C., G. M. Clark, R. K. Shepherd, S. J. O'Leary, and C. W. Walters. "Intracochlear Electrical Stimulation of Normal and Deaf Cats Investigated Using Brainstem Response Audiometry." *Acta Oto-Laryngologica* suppl 399 (1983): 5–17.

Black, R. C., A. C. Steel, and G. M. Clark. "Amplitude and Pulse Rate Difference Limens for Electrical Stimulation of the Cochlea Following Graded Degeneration of the Auditory Nerve." *Acta Oto-Laryngologica* 95 (1983): 27–33.

——. "Frequency Discrimination and the Spiral Ganglion Cell Population in Cats." *Proceedings of the Australian Physiological and Pharmacological Society* 12 (1981).

Blamey, P. J., and G. M. Clark. "A Wearable Multiple-Electrode Electrotactile Speech Processor for the Profoundly Deaf." *Journal of the Acoustical Society of America* 77 (1985): 1619–21.

Blamey, P. J., R. C. Dowell, Y. C. Tong, A. M. Brown, S. M. Luscombe, and G. M. Clark. "Speech Processing Studies Using an Acoustic Model of a Multiple-Channel Cochlear Implant." *Journal of the Acoustical Society of America* 76 (1984): 104–10.

Blamey, P. J., R. C. Dowell, Y. C. Tong, and G. M. Clark. "An Acoustic Model of a Multiple-Channel Cochlear Implant." *Journal of the Acoustical Society of America* 76 (1984): 97–103.

Bondarew, V., and P. Seligman. *The Cochlear Story.* eBook: CSIRO Publishing, 2012.

Brown, A. M., G. M. Clark, R. C. Dowell, L. F. Martin, and P. M. Seligman. "Telephone Use by a Multi-Channel Cochlear Implant Patient. An Evaluation Using Open-Set Cid Sentences." *Journal of Laryngology and Otology* 99 (1985): 231–38.

Busby, P. A., Y. C. Tong, and G. M. Clark. "Underlying Dimensions and Individual Differences in Auditory, Visual and Auditory-Visual Vowel Perception by Hearing Impaired Children." *Journal of the Acoustical Society of America* 75 (1984): 1858–65.

Chen, B. K., G. M. Clark, and R. Jones. "Evaluation of Trajectories and Contact Pressures for the Straight Nucleus Cochlear Implant Electrode Array—a Two-Dimensional Application of Finite Element Analysis." *Medical Engineering & Physics* 25, no. 2 (Mar 2003): 141–47.

Clark, G. M. "Cochlear Implant Research Directions." In *Cochlear Implants. XVI World Congress of Otorhinolaryngology Head and Neck Surgery*, edited by G.M. Clark, 55–60. Bologna: Monduzzi Editore, 1997.

———. *Cochlear Implants: Fundamentals and Applications*. New York: Springer, 2003.

———. "An Evaluation of Per-Scalar Cochlear Electrode Implantation Techniques. An Histopathogical Study in Cats." *Journal of Laryngology and Otology* 91 (1977): 185–99.

———. "A Hearing Prosthesis for Severe Perceptive Deafness-Experimental Studies." *Journal of Laryngology and Otology* 87 (1973): 929–45.

———. "Middle Ear and Neural Mechanisms in Hearing and in the Management of Deafness." PhD thesis, University of Sydney, 1969.

———. "Neurobiology." In *Cochlear Implants: Fundamentals and Applications*. New York: Springer, 2003.

———. "A Neurophysiological Assessment of the Surgical Treatment of Perceptive Deafness." *International Audiology* 9 (1970): 103–09.

———. "Personal Reflections on the Multichannel Cochlear Implant and a View of the Future." *Journal of Rehabilitation Reseaarch & Development* JRRD 45, no. 5 (2008): 651–93.

———. "The Principles of the Structural Support of the Nose and Their Application to Nasal and Septal Surgery." Master of Surgery thesis, University of Sydney, 1968.

———. "Responses of Cells in the Superior Olivary Complex of the Cat to Electrical Stimulation of the Auditory Nerve." *Experimental Neurology* 24 (1969): 124–36.

———. "The Role of the Nasal Septum in One-Stage Rhinoplasty." *Archives of Otolaryngology* 85 (1967): 418–23.

———. *Sounds from Silence*. Sydney: Allen and Unwin, 2000.

———. "Vesicle Shape Versus Type of Synapse in the Nerve Endings of the Ct Medial Superior Olive." *Brain Research* 15 (1969): 548–51.

Clark G. M. Black R., Dewhurst D. J., Forster I. C., Patrick J. F., Tong Y. C. "A Multiple Electrode Hearing Prosthesis for Cochlear Implantation in Deaf Patients." *Medical Progress Through Technology* 5 (1976): 127–140.

Clark, G. M., Blamey, P. J., Busby, P. A., Dowell, R. C., Franz, B. K., Musgrave, G. N., Nienhuys, T. G., Pyman, B. C., Roberts, S. A., Tong, Y. C. and Webb, R. L. "A Multiple-Electrode Intracochlear Implant for Children." *Archives of Otolaryngology–Head & Neck Surgery* 113, no. 8 (1987): 825–28.

Clark, G. M., Busby, P. A., Roberts, S. A., Dowell, R. C., Blamey, P. J., Mecklenburg, D. J., Webb, R. L., Pyman, B. C. and Franz, B. K. "Preliminary Results for the Cochlear Corporation Multielectrode Intracochlear Implant in Six Prelingually Deaf Patients." *American Journal of Otology* 8 (1987): 234–39.

Clark, G. M., J. C. M. Clark, and J. B. Furness. "The Evolving Science of Cochlear Implants." JAMA 310, no. 12 (2013): 1225–26.

Clark, G. M., P. A. Crosby, R. C. Dowell, J. A. Kuzma, D. K. Money, J. F. Patrick, P. M. Seligman, and Y. C. Tong. "The Preliminary Clinical Trial of a Multi-Channel Cochlear Implant Hearing Prosthesis." *Journal of the Acoustical Society of America* 74 (1983): 1911–14.

Clark, G. M., G. J. Dooley, and P. J. Blamey. "Combined Electrical and Acoustical Stimulation Using a Bimodal Speech Processor." In *American Pediatric Otolaryngological Society Meeting*. Hawaii, May 1991: presentation only, 1991.

Clark, G. M., R. C. Dowell, A. M. Brown, S. M. Luscombe, B. C. Pyman, R. L. Webb, Q. R. Bailey, P. M. Seligman, Y. C. Tong. . "Clinical Trial of a Multiple-Channel Cochlear Prosthesis: An Initial Study in Four Patients with Profound Total Hearing Loss." *Medical Journal of Australia* 2, no. 9 (1983): 430–33.

Clark, G. M., R. C. Dowell, B. C. Pyman, A. M. Brown, R. L. Webb, Y. C. Tong, and Q. R. Bailey. "Clinical Trial of a Multi-Channel Cochlear Prosthesis: Results on 10 Postlingually Deaf Patients." *Australian and New Zealand Journal of Surgery* 54 (1984): 519–26.

Clark, G. M., and C. W. Dunlop. "Middle Ear Sound Transmission: An Experimental Study." *Archives of Otolaryngology* 88, no. 5 (1968): 469–76.

Clark, G. M., R. J. Hallworth, and K. Zdanius. "A Cochlear Implant Electrode." *Journal of Laryngology and Otology* 89 (1975): 787–92.

Clark, G. M., H. G. Kranz, and H. Minas. "Behavioral Thresholds in the Cat to Frequency Modulated Sound and Electrical Stimulation of the Auditory Nerve." *Experimental Neurology* 41 (1973): 190–200.

Clark, G. M., B. C. Pyman, and R. E. Pavillard. "A Protocol for the Prevention of Infection in Cochlear Implant Surgery." *Journal of Laryngology and Otology* 94, no. 12 (1980): 1377–86.

Clark, G. M., B. C. Pyman, R. L. Webb, Q. E. Bailey, and R. K. Shepherd. "Surgery for an Improved Multiple-Channel Cochlear Implant." *Annals of Otology, Rhinology and Laryngology* 93, no. 3 Pt 1 (1984): 204–07.

Clark, G. M., R. K. Shepherd, B. K-H. G. Franz, and D. Bloom. "Intracochlear Electrode Implantation. Round Window Membrane Sealing Procedures and Permeability Studies." *Acta Oto-Laryngologica* Suppl 410 (1984): 5–15.

Clark, G. M., and Y. C. Tong. "Multiple-Electrode Cochlear Implant for Profound or Total Hearing Loss: A Review." *Medical Journal of Australia* 1 (1981): 428–29.

Clark, G. M., Y. C. Tong, Q. R. Bailey, R. C. Black, L. F. Martin, J. B. Millar, B. J. O'Loughlin, J. F. Patrick, and B. C. Pyman. "A Multiple-Electrode Cochlear Implant." *Journal of the Oto-Laryngological Society of Australia* 4 (1978): 208–12.

Clark, G. M., Y. C. Tong, and L. F. Martin. "A Multiple-Channel Cochlear Implant. An Evaluation Using Closed-Set Spondaic Words." *Journal of Laryngology and Otology* 95 (1981): 461–64.

——. "A Multiple-Channel Cochlear Implant. An Evaluation Using Open-Set Cid Sentences." *Laryngoscope* 91 (1981): 628–34.

Clark, G. M., Y. C. Tong, L. F. Martin, and P. A. Busby. "A Multiple-Channel Cochlear Implant. An Evaluation Using an Open-Set Word Test." *Acta Oto-Laryngologica* 91 (1981): 173–75.

Clark, G. M., Y. C. Tong, L. F.A. Martin, P. A. Busby, R. C. Dowell, P. M. Seligman, and J. F. Patrick. "A Multiple-Channel Cochlear Implant: An Evaluation Using Nonsense Syllables." *Annals of Otology, Rhinology and Laryngology* 90 (1981): 227–30.

Clark, G. M., Y. C. Tong, and J. F. Patrick. *Cochlear Prostheses.* Edinburgh: Churchill Livingstone, 1990.

Clark, G. M., Tong, Y. C., Harrison, J. M., Vandali, A. E., van Hoesel, R. J. M., Lim, H. H., Lai, W. K., Denison, M., Galvin, K., Hollow, R. D., McDermott, H. J., Cohen, L. . T., Wills, R. & Millar, J. B.. "Speech Processors for Auditory Prostheses." *Final Report, February 1–December 30,* NIH *Contract No1-DC-9-2400.* (1991).

Cohen, N. L., S. B. Waltzman, and S. G. Fisher. "A Prospective, Randomised Study of Cochlear Implants." *New England Journal of Medicine* 328 (1993): 233–82.

Collins, Francis S. *The Language of God: A Scientist Presents Evidence for Belief.* New York: Free Press, 2006.

Conway Morris, S. *Life's Solution: Inevitable Humans in a Lonely Universe.* Cambridge: Cambridge University Press, 2003.

Cowan, R. S. C., J. I. Alcantara, P. J. Blamey, and G. M. Clark. "Preliminary Evaluation of a Multichannel Electrotactile Speech Processor." *Journal of the Acoustical Society of America* 83 (1988): 2328.

Dahm, M., G. M. Clark, B. K-H. G. Franz, R. K. Shepherd, M. J. Burton, and R. Robins-Browne. "Cochlear Implantation in Children: Labyrinthitis Following Pneumococcal Otitis Media in Unimplanted and Implanted Cat Cochleas." *Acta Oto-Laryngologica* 114 (1994): 620–25.

Dahm, M., H. L. Seldon, B. C. Pyman, and G. M. Clark. "3D Reconstruction of the Temporal Bone in Cochlear Implant Surgery." In *Transplants and Implants in Otology II,* edited by N. Yanagihara and J. Suziki, 271–75. Amsterdam: Kugler Publications, 1992.

Dahm, M., R. K. Shepherd, and G. M. Clark. "The Postnatal Growth of the Temporal Bone and Its Implications for Cochlear Implantation in Children." *Acta Oto-Laryngologica,* no. suppl 505 (1993): 1–39.

Dawson, P., P. J. Blamey, G. M. Clark, P. A. Busby, L. C. Rowland, S. J. Dettman, A. M. Brown, et al., "Results in Children Using the 22 Electrode Cochlear Implant." *Journal of the Acoustical Society of America* 86, no. Suppl 1 (1989): 81.

Djourno, A., and C. Eyries. "Prosthese Auditive Par Excitation Electrique a Distance Du Nerf Sensoriel a L'aide D'un Bobinage Includ a Demeure." *Presse Medicale* 35 (1957): 14–17.

Dooley, G. J., P. J. Blamey, P. M. Seligman, J. I. Alcantara, G. M. Clark, J. K. Shallop, P. Arndt, J. N. Heller, and C. M. Menapace. "Combined Electrical and Acoustic Stimulation Using a Bimodal Prosthesis." *Archives of Otolaryngology-Head and Neck Surgery* 119 (1993): 55–60.

Dormer, K. J., G. L. Richard, and J. V. D. Hough. "The Use of Rare-Earth Magnet Couplers in Cochlear Implants." *Laryngoscope* 91, no. 11 (1981): 1812–20.

Dowell, R. C., L. A. Whitford, P. M. Seligman, B. K-H. G. Franz, G. M. Clark. "Preliminary Results with a Miniature Speech Processor for the 22-Electrode/Cochlear Hearing Prosthesis." In *Otorhinolaryngology, Head and Neck Surgery,* edited by T. Sacristan, 1167–73. Amsterdam: Kugler and Ghedini, 1990.

Dowell, R. C., D. J. Mecklenburg, and G. M. Clark. "Speech Recognition for 40 Patients Receiving Multichannel Cochlear Implants." *Archives of Otolaryngology* 112 (1986): 1054–59.

Dowell, R. C., J. F. Patrick, P. J. Blamey, P. M. Seligman, D. K. Money, and G. M. Clark. "Signal Processing in Quiet and Noise." In *Cochlear Implant: Current Situation*, edited by P. Banfai, 495–98, 1987.

Dowell, R. C., P. M. Seligman, P. J. Blamey, and G. M. Clark. "Evaluation of a Two-Formant Speech-Processing Strategy for a Multichannel Cochlear Prosthesis." *Annals of Otology, Rhinology and Laryngology* 96 (suppl. 128) (1987): 132–133.

Dowell, R. C., P. M. Seligman, P. J. Blamey, and G. M. Clark. "Speech Perception Using a Two-Formant 22-Electrode Cochlear Prosthesis in Quiet and in Noise." *Acta Oto-Laryngologica* 104, no. 5–6 (1987): 439–46.

Dowell, R. C., R. L. Webb, and G. M. Clark. "Clinical Results Using a Multiple-Channel Cochlear Prosthesis." *Acta Oto-Laryngologica* (1984): 230–36.

Epstein, J. *The Story of the Bionic Ear.* South Yarra: Hylands House, 1989: 1–144.

Forster, I. C. "The Bioengineering Development of a Multi-Channel, Implantable Hearing Prosthesis for the Profoundly Deaf." In *PhD thesis.* The University of Melbourne Department of Electrical Engineering, 1978.

Franz, B. K-H. G., G. M. Clark, and D. Bloom. "Permeability of the Implanted Round Window Membrane in the Cat-an Investigation Using Horseradish Peroxidase." *Acta Oto-Laryngologica* suppl 410 (1984): 17–23.

Gantz, B. J., B. F. McCabe, R. S. Tyler, and J. P. Preece. "Evaluation of Four Cochlear Implant Designs." *Annals of Otology, Rhinology and Laryngology* 96 (1987): 145–47.

Gantz, B. J., R. S. Tyler, J. F. Knutson, G. Woodworth, P. Abbas, B. F. McCabe, J. Hinricks, et al., "Evaluation of Five Different Cochlear Implant Designs: Audiologic Assessment and Predictors of Performance." *Laryngoscope* 98 (1988): 1100–06.

Gillen, M., *The Search for John Small, First Fleeter.* Sydney: Library of Australian History, 1985.

Goodhill, V. "Progress in Otology." *Annals of Otology, Rhinology and Laryngology* 88 (1979): 658–63.

Lawrence, M. "Direct Stimulation of Auditory Nerve Fibers." *Archives of Otolaryngology* 80 (1964): 367–68.

MacKay, D. M. *The Open Mind and Other Essays.* Grand Rapids: Inter-Varsity Press, 1988.

McDermott, H. J., C. M. Mckay, and A. E. Vandali. "A New Portable Sound Processor for the University of Melbourne/ Nucleus Limited Multielectrode Cochlear Implant." *The Journal of the Acoustical Society of America* 91, no. 6 (1992): 3367–71.

McKay, C. M., H. J. McDermott, A. Vandali, and G. M. Clark. "A Comparison of Speech Perception of Cochlear Implantees Using the Spectral Maxima Sound Processor (Smsp) and the Msp (Multipeak) Processor." *Acta Oto-Laryngologica* 112 (1992): 752–61.

Mecklenburg, D. J., P. A. Busby, S. A. Roberts, R. C. Dowell, G. N. Musgrave, P. J. Blamey, Y. C. Tong, et al., "Results in Multiple-Electrode Cochlear Implants in Children." In *Cochlear implant: current situation*, edited by P. Banfai, 481–85. Düren, Germany, 1987.

Mollie, G. *The Search for John Small-First Fleeter.* Sydney: Library of Australian History, 1985.

Nienhuys, T. G. W., G. N. Musgrave, P. A. Busby, P. J. Blamey, P. Nott, Y. C. Tong, R. C. Dowell, and G. M. Clark. "Educational Assessment and Management of Children with Multichannel Cochlear Implants." *Annals of Otology, Rhinology and Laryngology* 96, no. Suppl 128 (1987): 80–82.

Nystrand, A. "Kokleaimplantat Ger Allt Bättre Resultat." *Lakartidningen* 37, no. 103 (2006): 2616–19.

Paolini, A. G., and G. M. Clark. "Intracellular Responses of the Rat Anteroventral Cochlear Nucleus to Intracochlear Electrical Stimulation." *Brain Research Bulletin* 46, no. 4 (1998): 317–27.

Polkinghorne, J. *Quarks, Chaos and Christianity: Questions to Science and Religion, Revised Edition."* New York: Crossroad Publishing, 2006.

Reefhuis, J., M. A. Honein, C. G. Whitney, S. Chamany, E. A. Mann, K. R. Biernath, K. Broder, et al., "Risk of Bacterial Meningitis in Children with Cochlear Implants." *New England Journal of Medicine* 349, no. 5 (2003): 435–45.

Rickards, F. W., and G. M. Clark. "Steady-State Evoked Potentials to Amplitude-Modulated Tones." In *Evoked Potentials II*, edited by R.H. Anodar and C. Barber, 163–68. Boston: Butterworths, 1984.

Rickards, F. W., and G. M. Clark. "Steady State Evoked Potentials to Amplitude Modulated Tones." *Proceedings of the Australian Physiological and Pharmacological Society* 13, no. 2 (1982).

Rose, J. E., J. F. Brugge, D. J. Anderson, and J. E. Hind. "Phase-Locked Response to Low-Frequency Tones in Single Auditory Nerve Fibers of the Squirrel Monkey." *Journal of Neurophysiology* 30 (1967): 769–93.

Scrivener, B. P., W. P. R. Gibson. "Cochlear Implant after Radical Mastoidectomy." *Annals of Otology, Rhinology and Laryngology* (1987): 19–20.

Shepherd, R. K., G. M. Clark, and R. C. Black. "Chronic Electrical Stimulation of the Auditory Nerve in Cats. Physiological and Histopathological Results." *Acta Oto-Laryngologica*, no. suppl 399 (1983): 19–31.

Shepherd, R. K., G. M. Clark, R. C. Black, and J. F. Patrick. "Chronic Electrical Stimulation of the Auditory Nerve in Cats." *Proceedings of the Australian Physiological and Pharmacological Society* 13 (1982): 211P.

Shepherd, R. K., G. M. Clark, R. C. Black, and J. F. Patrick. "The Histopathological Effects of Chronic Electrical Stimulation of the Cat Cochlea." *Journal of Laryngology and Otology* 97 (1983): 333–41.

Shepherd, R. K., S.A. Xu, B. K.-H. G. Franz, Y. C. Tong, G. M. Clark, S. Hatsushika, R. E. Millard, et al. "Studies on Pediatric Auditory Prosthesis Implants. Seventh Quarterly Progress Report." NIH *Contract No. 1-NS-7-2342* (1989).

Simmons, F. B., C. J. Monegeon, W. R. Lewis, and D. A. Huntington. "Electrical Stimulation of Acoustical Nerve and Inferior Colliculus." *Archives of Otolaryngology* 79 (1964): 559–67.

Skinner, M. W., G. M. Clark, L. A. Whitford, P. M. Seligman, S. J. Staller, D. B. Shipp, J. K. Shallop, et al., "Evaluation of a New Spectral Peak Coding Strategy for the Nucleus 22 Channels Cochlear Implant System." *American Journal of Otology* 15 (1994): 15–27.

Skinner, M. W., L. K. Holden, L. A. Whitford, K. L. Plant, C. Psarros, and T. A. Holden. "Speech Recognition with the Nucleus 24 Speak, Ace, and Cis Speech Coding Strategies in Newly Implanted Adults." *Ear and Hearing* 23, no. 3 (2002): 207–23.

*The Small Family in Australia, 1788–1988*. Epping, NSW: John & Mary Small Descendant Association, 1974.

Thomas, B. W. *The Thomas Family of Guyong, NSW: 1849–1929*. Wahroonga, NSW: B. W. Thomas, 1974.

Tong, Y. C., R. C Black, ., G. M. Clark, I. C. Forster, J. B. Millar, B. J. O'Loughlin, and J. F. Patrick. "A Preliminary Report on a Multiple-Channel Cochlear Implant Operation." *Journal of Laryngology and Otology* 93 (1979): 679–95.

Tong, Y. C., P. A. Busby, and G. M. Clark. "Perceptual Studies on Cochlear Implant Patients with Early Onset of Profound Hearing Impairment Prior to Normal Development of Auditory, Speech, and Language Skills." *Journal of the Acoustical Society of America* 84 (1988): 951–62.

Tong, Y. C., G. M. Clark, P. J. Blamey, P. A. Busby, and R. C. Dowell. "Psychophysical Studies for Two Multiple-Channel Cochlear Implant Patients." *Journal of the Acoustical Society of America* 71 (1982): 153–60.

Tong, Y. C., G. M. Clark, P. M. Seligman, and J. F. Patrick. "Speech Processing for a Multiple-Electrode Cochlear Implant Hearing Prosthesis." *Journal of the Acoustical Society of America* 68 (1980): 1897–99.

Tong, Y. C., R. C. Dowell, P. J. Blamey, and G. M. Clark. "Two-Component Hearing Sensations Produced by Two-Electrode Stimulation in the Cochlea of a Deaf Patient." *Science* 219 (1983): 993–94.

Tong, Y. C., W. K. Lai, M. Denison, A. Vandali, H. H. Lim, J. M. Harrison, H. J. McDermott, R. D. Hollow, and G. M. Clark. "Speech Processors for Auditory Prostheses. Third Quarterly Progress Report." NIH 1-DC-9-2400 (1989).

van Hoesel, R. J. M. "Bilateral Electrical Stimulation with Multi-Channel Cochlear Implants." The University of Melbourne, 1998.

van Hoesel, R. J. M., and G. M. Clark. "Fusion and Lateralization Study with Two Binaural Cochlear Implant Patients." *Annals of Otology, Rhinology and Laryngology* 104, no. Suppl 166 (1995): 233–35.

———. "Speech Results with a Bilateral Multi-Channel Cochlear Implant Subject for Spatially Separated Signal and Noise." *Australian Journal of Audiology* 21 (1999): 23–28.

van Hoesel, R. J. M., Y. C. Tong, R. D. Hollow, and G. M. Clark. "Psychophysical and Speech Perception Studies: A Case Report on a Binaural Cochlear Implant Subject." *Journal of the Acoustical Society of America* 94 (1993): 3178–89.

Webb, R. L., R. C. Dowell, G. M. Clark, B. C. Pyman, A. M. Brown, Y. C. Tong, P. M. Seligman, P. J. Blamey, and S. Xu. "The Multi-Channel Cochlear Implant." *Journal of the Oto-Laryngological Society of Australia* 5 (1985): 273–76.

Williams, A. J., G. M. Clark, and G. V. Stanley. "Behavioural Responses in the Cat to Simple Patterns of Electrical Stimulation of the Terminal Auditory Nerve Fibres." *Proceedings of the Australian Physiological and Pharmacological Society* 5, no. 2 (1974): 252.

———. "Pitch Discrimination in the Cat through Electrical Stimulation of the Terminal Auditory Nerve Fibers." *Physiological Psychology* 4 (1976): 23–27.

Wilson, B. S., D. T. Lawson, M. Zerbi, and C. C. Finley. "Speech Processors for Auditory Prostheses. Twelfth Quarterly Progress Report." *NIH Contract* No1-DC-9-2401 (1992).

Wilson, B. S., C. C. Finley, D. T. Lawson, R. D. Wolford, D. K. Eddington, and W. M. Rabinowitz. "Better Speech Recognition with Cochlear Implants." *Nature* 352, no. 6332 (1991): 236–38.

Xu, S., R. C. Dowell, and G. M. Clark. "Results for Chinese and English in a Multichannel Cochlear Implant Patient." *Annals of Otology, Rhinology and Laryngology* 96, no. Suppl 128 (1987): 126–27.

# Notes

1   *The Age*, 23 January 1970.

2   Clark, *Cochlear Implants*.

3   Ibid.

4   Rickards and Clark, "Steady-State Evoked Potentials."

5   Reminiscences of Colin Clark, in the Graeme Clark Collection, National Library of Australia.

6   Thomas, *The Thomas Family of Guyong*.

7   *The Small Family in Australia, 1788–1988*. The story of the Small family has been written up by my mother's cousin in Gillen, *The Search for John Small*.

8   Graeme Clark's addition to Alfred Youdale's letters donated to the Australian War Memorial in 2019.

9   From an extract entitled *Untold Stories: Footprints of an Achiever* by John Wigley, Vice President of the Camden Historical Society (published in the *Sydney Morning Herald* approximately 21 May 2002).

10  Clark, "The Role of the Nasal Septum in One-Stage Rhinoplasty."

11  Clark, "The Principles of the Structural Support of the Nose." "The Role of the Nasal Septum in One-Stage Rhinoplasty."

12  Simmons et al., "Electrical Stimulation of Acoustical Nerve and Inferior Colliculus."

13  Lawrence, "Direct Stimulation of Auditory Nerve Fibers," ibid. 80.

14  Goodhill, "Progress in Otology."

15  Djourno and Eyries, "Prosthese Auditive Par Excitation Electrique."

16  Rose et al., "Phase-Locked Response to Low-Frequency Tones."

17  Otto Schmitt was an American engineer and biophysicist who played a key role in establishing the field of biomedical engineering.

18  It was pleasing many years later to receive the 2009 Otto Schmitt Award, from The International Federation of Medical and Biological Engineering (for exceptional contributions to the advancement of the field of medical and biological engineering), presented every three years at the World Congress on Medical Physics and Biomedical Engineering.

19  Clark, "Vesicle Shape Versus Type of Synapse."

20  Clark, "Middle Ear and Neural Mechanisms." Clark and Dunlop, "Middle Ear Sound Transmission."

21  Clark, "Middle Ear and Neural Mechanisms."

22  Rickards and Clark, "Steady State Evoked Potentials," 1982. Rickards and Clark, "Steady-State Evoked Potentials," 1984.

23  Clark, "Responses of Cells in the Superior Olivary Complex."

24  Clark, "A Neurophysiological Assessment of the Surgical Treatment of Perceptive Deafness." Clark, "Middle Ear and Neural Mechanisms in Hearing and the Management of Deafness."

25  Clark, "Middle Ear and Neural Mechanisms in Hearing and in the Management of Deafness."

26  Clark, Kranz, and H. Minas, "Behavioral Thresholds in the Cat."

27  Ibid. Clark, "A Hearing Prosthesis for Severe Perceptive Deafness-Experimental Studies."

28  Williams, Clark, and Stanley, "Behavioural Responses in the Cat." "Pitch Discrimination in the Cat."

29  Black, Steel, and Clark, "Amplitude and Pulse Rate Difference Limens." "Frequency Discrimination and the Spiral Ganglion Cell Population in Cats."

30  Black and Clark, "Electrical Transmission Line Properties of the Cat Cochlea."

31  Clark, Hallworth, and Zdanius, "A Cochlear Implant Electrode."

32  Clark, "An Evaluation of Per-Scalar Cochlear Electrode Implantation Techniques."

33  Ibid.

34  Chen, Clark, and Jones, "Evaluation of Trajectories and Contact Pressures."

35  Clark et al., "A Multiple Electrode Hearing Prosthesis." Clark, "A Hearing Prosthesis for Severe Perceptive Deafness-Experimental Studies."

36  Shepherd et al., "Chronic Electrical Stimulation of the Auditory Nerve in Cats," 1982. Shepherd et al., "Chronic Electrical Stimulation of the Auditory Nerve in Cats," 1983. Shepherd, et al., "The Histopathological Effects of Chronic Electrical Stimulation of the Cat Cochlea."

37  These issues are discussed in the chapter "Surgical Pathology" in Clark, *Cochlear Implants*. See also Clark, "Personal Reflections on the Multichannel Cochlear Implant," figures 9 and 17.

38  Franz, Clark, and Bloom, "Permeability of the Implanted Round Window Membrane." M. Dahm et al., "Cochlear Implantation in Children."

39  Forster, "The Bioengineering Development of a Multi-Channel."

40  Epstein, "The Story of the Bionic Ear."

41  Clark, Clark, and Furness, "The Evolving Science of Cochlear Implants."

42  Jim Unger, Universal Press Syndicate, 1978.

43  Ainsworth, *Mechanisms of Speech Recognition*.

44  The vocoder analyses and synthesises the human voice and was invented by Homer Dudley at Bell Labs in 1938.

45  Clark, Pyman, and Pavillard, "A Protocol for the Prevention of Infection in Cochlear Implant Surgery."

46  Clark et al., "A Multiple-Electrode Cochlear Implant." Tong et al., "A Preliminary Report on a Multiple-Channel Cochlear Implant Operation." Tong et al., "Speech Processing for a Multiple-Electrode Cochlear."

47  Clark, *Sounds from Silence*.

48  Clark and Tong, "Multiple-Electrode Cochlear Implant for Profound or Total Hearing Loss." Clark, Tong, and Martin, "A Multiple-Channel Cochlear Implant. An Evaluation Using Open-Set Cid Sentences." "A Multiple-Channel Cochlear Implant. An Evaluation Using Closed-Set Spondaic Words." Clark et al., "A Multiple-Channel Cochlear Implant. An Evaluation Using an Open-Set Word Test." Clark et al., "A Multiple-Channel Cochlear Implant: An Evaluation Using Nonsense Syllables."

49  Bondarew and Seligman, *The Cochlear Story*.

50  Tong et al., "Psychophysical Studies for Two Multiple-Channel Cochlear Implant Patients."

51 Clark, *Sounds from Silence*. Clark and Tong, "Multiple-Electrode Cochlear Implant for Profound or Total Hearing Loss: A Review." Clark, Tong, and Martin, "A Multiple-Channel Cochlear Implant. An Evaluation Using Closed-Set Spondaic Words." Clark et al., "A Multiple-Channel Cochlear Implant. An Evaluation Using an Open-Set Word Test."

52 Clark et al., "Surgery for an Improved Multiple-Channel Cochlear Implant."

53 Clark et al., "The Preliminary Clinical Trial of a Multi-Channel Cochlear Implant Hearing Prosthesis."

54 Dowell et al., "Clinical Trial of a Multiple-Channel Cochlear Prosthesis: An Initial Study."

55 Clark et al., "Clinical Trial of a Multi-Channel Cochlear Prosthesis: Results on 10 Postlingually Deaf Patients."

56 Dowell, Webb, and Clark, "Clinical Results Using a Multiple-Channel Cochlear Prosthesis."

57 Brown et al., "Telephone Use by a Multi-Channel Cochlear Implant Patient."

58 Xu, Dowell, and Clark, "Results for Chinese and English in a Multichannel Cochlear Implant Patient."

59 Gantz et al., "Evaluation of Five Different Cochlear Implant Designs." Gantz et al., "Evaluation of Four Cochlear Implant Designs."

60 Webb et al., "The Multi-Channel Cochlear Implant."

61 Dowell, Mecklenburg, and Clark, "Speech Recognition for 40 Patients."

62 Clark, "Cochlear Implant Research Directions," in *Cochlear Implants. XVI World Congress.*

63 Ibid.

64 Blamey et al., "An Acoustic Model of a Multiple-Channel Cochlear Implant." Blamey et al., "Speech Processing Studies Using an Acoustic Model."

65 Dowell et al., "Evaluation of a Two-Formant Speech Processing Strategy." Dowell et al., "Speech Perception Using a Two-Formant 22-Electrode Cochlear Prosthesis."

66 Dowell et al., "Preliminary Results with a Miniature Speech Processor," in *Otorhinolaryngology, Head and Neck Surgery.*

67 Cohen, Waltzman, and Fisher, "A Prospective, Randomised Study of Cochlear Implants."

68 Tong et al., "Speech Processors for Auditory Prostheses. Third Quarterly Progress Report." Clark et al., "Speech Processors for Auditory Prostheses," *Final Report.*

69 McDermott, Mckay, and Vandali, "A New Portable Sound Processor for the University of Melbourne." McKay et al., "A Comparison of Speech Perception of Cochlear Implantees."

70 Skinner et al., "Evaluation of a New Spectral Peak Coding Strategy."

71 Wilson et al., "Better Speech Recognition with Cochlear Implants." Wilson et al., "Speech Processors for Auditory Prostheses. Twelfth Quarterly Progress Report."

72 Black et al., "Intracochlear Electrical Stimulation of Normal and Deaf Cats."

73 Shepherd, Clark, and Black, "Chronic Electrical Stimulation of the Auditory Nerve in Cats."

74 Clark, "Personal Reflections on the Multichannel Cochlear Implant."

75 van Hoesel et al., "Psychophysical and Speech Perception Studies." "Bilateral Electrical Stimulation with Multi-Channel Cochlear Implants." van Hoesel and Clark, "Fusion and Lateralization Study with Two Binaural Cochlear Implant Patients." "Speech Results

with a Bilateral Multi-Channel Cochlear Implant Subject."

76 Clark, Dooley, and Blamey, "Combined Electrical and Acoustical Stimulation." G. J. Dooley et al., "Combined Electrical and Acoustical Stimulation Using a Bimodal Prosthesis."

77 Tong, Busby, and Clark, "Perceptual Studies on Cochlear Implant Patients with Early Onset."

78 Busby, Tong, and Clark, "Underlying Dimensions and Individual Differences in Auditory."

79 Nienhuys et al., "Educational Assessment and Management of Children with Multichannel Cochlear Implants."

80 Clark et al., "Intracochlear Electrode Implantation. Round Window Membrane Sealing."

81 Shepherd et al., "Studies on Pediatric Auditory Prosthesis Implants. Seventh Quarterly Progress Report."

82 Reefhuis et al., "Risk of Bacterial Meningitis in Children with Cochlear Implants."

83 For further details refer to the Graeme Clark Collection, National Library of Australia.

84 An analysis of the first 19 children who had a Nucleus cochlear implant and also had meningitis are discussed in detail in Clark, *Cochlear Implants: Fundamentals and Applications*.

85 Blamey and Clark, "A Wearable Multiple-Electrode Electrotactile Speech Processor."

86 Cowan et al., "Preliminary Evaluation of a Multichannel Electrotactile Speech Processor."

87 Dormer, Richard, and Hough, "The Use of Rare-Earth Magnet Couplers in Cochlear Implants."

88 Clark, et al., "A Multiple-Electrode Intracochlear Implant for Children." Clark, et al., "Preliminary Results for the Cochlear Corporation Multielectrode Intracochlear Implant."

89 Dawson et al., "Results in Children Using the 22 Electrode Cochlear Implant."

90 Mecklenburg et al., "Results in Multiple-Electrode Cochlear Implants in Children."

91 Graeme Clark slides in the Graeme Clark Collection, National Library of Australia.

92 Dahm et al., "3D Reconstruction of the Temporal Bone in Cochlear Implant Surgery." Dahm, Shepherd, and Clark, "The Postnatal Growth of the Temporal Bone."

93 Annual Reports of the UoM/BEI in the Graeme Clark Collection, National Library Australia.

94 As the Honourable Peter Howson CBE has said in one of his recorded interviews, now in the Graeme Clark Collection, National Library of Australia.

95 Polkinghorne, *Quarks, Chaos and Christianity: Questions to Science and Religion.*

96 Collins, *The Language of God: A Scientist Presents Evidence for Belief.*

97 MacKay, *The Open Mind and Other Essays.*

98 Conway Morris, *Life's Solution: Inevitable Humans in a Lonely Universe.*

99 Alexander, *Creation or Evolution: Do We Have to Choose?* Denis Alexander is Emeritus Director of the Faraday Institute for Science and Religion, St Edmund's College, Cambridge.

# Index